Pamela McKenzie is a healthy, active mother of four living in the southwest of Western Australia, without any previous health condition. There was no reason to suspect that there was any cause for concern on Easter morning 2014, but later that morning, she suffered a rare form of heart attack (SCAD). She then set herself the task of finding as many other survivors as possible. What she found were more people that felt alone and isolated and this has now sparked Australian research into SCAD. TV appearances, magazine articles and radio interviews now under her belt, this book is the realisation of not being alone for the survivors of SCAD.

Dedication

I'd like to dedicate this book to my husband, family and friends who believed in me even when I didn't. I really can't thank you enough for your unconditional love and support, without which I never could have made it this far.

Pamela McKenzie

SCAD STRAIGHT FROM THE HEART

AUSTIN MACAULEY PUBLISHERS™

LONDON • CAMBRIDGE • NEW YORK • SHARJAH

A CIP catalogue record for this title is available from the British Library.

ISBN 9781528901734 (Paperback)
ISBN 9781528901741 (E-Book)

www.austinmacauley.com

First Published (2018)
Austin Macauley Publishers Ltd™
25 Canada Square Canary Wharf
London
E14 5LQ

Acknowledgements

Without the donations and support from the following people and businesses, this book would have not been possible. A very big thank you goes out to the following:

Prof Robert Graham AO, FAA, Fahams MD

Cardiac Research Institute

Rosewood Care Group

Dominique Chevrant Breton

Naomi Byles

Cathran Bowyer

Susan North

Marty Chapman

Marianne Punshon

Lynne Clarke

Louden family

Dibdibn/Dilland family

Karen Heerman

Graham Lee

Introduction

The reasons for this book about SCAD are:

1. To assist newly-diagnosed patients with adjusting to life after SCAD
2. To assist family members and friends of SCAD patients to learn about the emotional journey after SCAD
3. To educate the general public about SCAD and the emotional journey of those who have had SCAD
4. To raise funding for SCAD research within Australia.

There is currently very minimal information available for those who are diagnosed with SCAD and this can be very frustrating.

Contained within this book are personal stories of SCAD patients who have chosen to share their journeys so that others can gain confidence with dealing with life after SCAD. It is also our hope that this book will assist the families of SCAD patients to understand the condition and the emotional effect that it has.

To suffer a life-changing heart attack for what apparently seems to be 'no real reason' can be very difficult to deal with. We would like to share our stories to raise awareness and assist others to realise that they are not alone, and that there are others of us out here if they would like to reach out and make contact. We would like to reassure all new SCAD patients that there definitely is life after SCAD and that although it is very frightening and difficult to deal with initially, you most definitely can pick up and keep going.

Within this book are some incredible stories of survival by some very amazing women; we hope you find them to be inspiring and valuable whether or not you yourself are a SCAD survivor.

At the end of this book, there are link addresses for further information and support groups as well as a section where you can write down your notes during your hospital stay so that you have a record that you can refer back to should you need to. In general, patients tend to only retain approx. 10%–20% of the information given to them by medical staff, so this is just to assist you for your future reference.

As a survivor of SCAD myself, I would like to also suggest that you consider keeping a diary to write in regarding your progress and your feelings as this can be very therapeutic. I found writing down your emotions and progress helps on bad days when you can look back and see how far you have really come.

We hope that you find this book to be helpful and informative.

By purchasing a copy of this book, you are helping to fund SCAD research here in Australia; we thank you for your support.

.

What Is SCAD?

Spontaneous Coronary Artery Dissection – SCAD – is an uncommon cardiac event that occurs when a tear forms in one or more of the coronary arteries near the heart. Pieces of the arterial wall can act as a flap or even block the artery by causing clotting. The clot or flap stops the flow of blood to the heart muscle resulting in a heart attack or even sudden death.

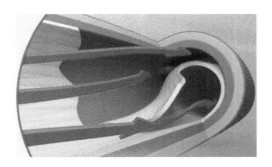

SCAD tends to affect mainly women aged 30 to 50, though it can occur at any age and to any gender. People who experience SCAD are often healthy, don't have any high-risk factors for heart disease such as high blood pressure, overweight, high cholesterol or diabetes.

To date, many medical practitioners are still unaware of the prevalence of SCAD and assume it to be rare. Studies and awareness are being raised within Australia with the hopes of educating both medical practitioners and the general public; many thanks to the tireless dedication of the Victor Chang Cardiac Research Institute.

Below is a graph of known survivors' location by state/territory within Australia. This information is correct at the time of print. Please note that this is only a list of those survivors who are known and have registered their whereabouts. There may be many more survivors who have not been listed.

Unfortunately, this graph does show that we still have a lot of work to do with raising awareness in areas such as the Northern Territory, South Australia and Tasmania.

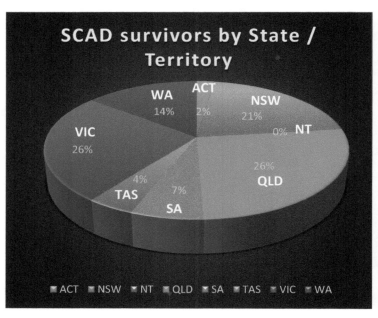

ACT – Australian Capital Territory, NSW – New South Wales, NT – Northern Territory, QLD – Queensland, SA – South Australia, TAS – Tasmania, Vic – Victoria, WA – Western Australia

Becky Baxter – 9th August 2017 – Aged 38

I had my SCAD attack Wednesday, 9th August 2017. Writing this at 38 years of age is something I never thought I'd be doing. The emotions are still so very raw. I have been married for nine years and we have two wonderful children, our son, aged nine, and daughter, aged six. I have always been a reasonably fit, healthy, happy person and not normally one to be bothered by stress but over the last two years, I have been dealing with a lot of emotional stress, which impacted all aspects of my life a great deal.

A few months prior to the attack, I had been having some time away from any major exercise due to emotionally needing a break and self-care can often mean taking myself away and just resting. Although still in a constant state of fight or flight, I had begun to really push through those emotions again and had started back at yoga and gym classes. The week before and days prior to my attack, I had been to yoga, worked extra shifts at work and started a higher-intensity workout and was feeling so positive in my mind and body.

Wednesday morning, I was sitting, relaxing on the lounge, organising a lunch date for my husband and I when a sudden intense pressure came on in my head, jaw and roof of my mouth, flowing down into my throat and chest, restricting my breathing. I knew something was really wrong, I tried to have a glass of water, hoping it would pass; it didn't. Heart palpitations started and I tried to breathe through it and not panic but I became very dizzy and the pressure on my chest continued. I laid down and rang my husband but he didn't answer, so I googled the Heart Foundation website and looked up symptoms of heart attacks in women as I knew they were different to men, only to see I had every symptom. My husband rang back within minutes and thankfully was already on his way home, we headed straight to the local hospital, as we only live a two-minute drive from it.

The first bloods taken were a negative for troponin, so I was sure I'd be heading home and so were the nurses, because honestly, I'm a fit, healthy 38-year-old; clearly it was just a panic attack or a stress-related reaction. I know that was what the staff were thinking but part of me knew, as much as I didn't want to believe it, it was more than that, but to be honest, I didn't think it could be an actual heart attack. Second bloods taken were a positive for troponin. They, the doctors and nursing staff, were in shock; I just sat there calmly, taking it all in. Why I was so calm, I don't know, disbelief maybe, but honestly, I'm the type of person who once I know what is going on, good or bad, and what I need to do, survival mode kicks in and I just deal with it, and in reality, I knew panicking was not going to help or reverse what just happened, so I just sat and listened, I listened to them tell me I had just had a cardiac event, I'd just had a heart attack.

I was transferred to Flinders Medical Centre that night and had an angiogram the next day. SCAD, Spontaneous Coronary Artery Dissection, is what they came back with, I had never heard of it. Although my cardiologist believes it is SCAD and contacted two other colleagues in the field, as there was still a possibility it could be plaque build-up, they too agreed SCAD as I have low cholesterol, I'm not diabetic and no family history of heart disease. Thankfully my attack was only minor, my left side of my heart all showed normal but my right had a 90% blockage, so I am being treated with Aspirin at this stage, but also on Rosuvastatin just as a precaution.

I was sent home the Friday, feeling a little lost now, as although I knew I'd had the heart attack and had accepted it, the resources for SCAD, causes, recovery, treatment, etc., are still limited and a great deal more research is still needed.

It had been almost a week since the attack and I was feeling well. Then Tuesday I felt that same scary pressure and pains I had before but thankfully, an attack was ruled out.

They also did an ultrasound for fluid around the heart as I was and still do experience shortness of breath, but that also came back clear. I was kept in overnight at my local hospital but all my tests were good and I was cleared to go home.

I was home again but feeling overwhelmed. Is this how my life is going to be now, constant trips to ED every time a pain or tightness occurs?

It has only been four weeks since my attack and still unsure of heart damage, long-term treatment and, honestly, what lies ahead and the battle with my emotions, anger, thankfulness, sadness, guilt, but I have made an appointment with a psychologist to help work through these and I begin cardiac rehab in two weeks' time to regain my confidence within my body and its strength.

It's only early days, so I know I need to be kind to myself. I'm so very thankful though to have found the support group Australian SCAD Survivors on Facebook; the support, knowledge and kindness shown helps to feel not so alone.

Louanne Mitchell – January 2014 – Aged 46

I did it, I did it, I did it! It was February 2017 and I had completed the Cole Classic, a one-kilometre Ocean Swim from Manly to Shelley Beach in NSW. My adrenalin was pumping and I celebrated with joy, hugs with my swimming buddies and a few obligatory selfies. As we wandered along the beachfront making our way home, I felt small tears well up inside me, as I reflected on my personal achievement. I had overcome physical and emotional limitations to get to this point and I was experiencing deep joy and satisfaction.

Just over three years earlier, in January 2014, I suffered a SCAD – Spontaneous Coronary Artery Dissection – and I had to withdraw from that year's ocean swim. I was disappointed but that was only one of the many emotions I experienced following my SCAD event.

I had switched to swimming as my exercise after suffering from meningitis in 2009. During this time, they discovered a cerebral aneurysm but I will leave that story for another time. After neurosurgery to have a stent implanted, in late 2009, I was no longer comfortable running, so I switched to swimming for my exercise. My goal was to one day complete an ocean swim and to never take good health for granted again.

Skip to January 2014, I was 47 years old, a wife, mother (of three children) and working full time. I was swimming a kilometre thirty-four times a week in preparation for the Cole Classic. My family and I had returned from ten days' camping; once we had the unpacked, we headed down to the beach for a swim. I swam in the surf with my nine-year-old daughter and as I emerged from the water, I had what I could only describe as double vision and I couldn't quite get my bearings to find my way back to our towels. My husband

16

asked me if I was OK because I looked like a confused old woman coming out of the surf. I was not impressed with his comment and said I was 'fine'.

Driving home, I had a tightness behind my left ear that came down my neck to the top of my chest. It lasted a few minutes. I wanted to ignore it but thought that I'd better tell my husband, Brett, and the kids that I had a funny pain but still assuring them that it was nothing.

I went inside, laid down for five minutes – sandy and still in wet swimmers – until it went away. I then had shower and a nap but as I woke, the tightness was there again, this time a little stronger and further into my chest. I told my husband, who suggested I call my best friend who is a GP. I said, 'Yeah yeah,' and went and got changed back into my swimmers to head back to the beach pool for some training. Deep down, I didn't want to be sick, well no one does really. I had been so sick in 2009 so I refused to believe it was possible there to be something else wrong with me.

The kids and I headed back to the beach. They walked around the rocks to the surf beach; I had never let them do this before and I jumped in the pool prepared to swim a kilometre. I swam a few laps and the tightness started again. I stopped swimming, walked out of the pool, trying really hard not to clutch my chest and draw attention to myself. This time, the tightness was stronger and lasted longer. I sat on the side of the pool until it stopped and then I rang my girlfriend, Kath. She was ridiculously calm and told me that I needed to go straight to the hospital with any kind of chest pain – who knew that chest pain often gets overlooked in women, particularly in younger women.

I was not impressed. I was at the pool, on my own and my kids are on the other side of the beach, in the surf. Fortunately, my daughter came running back to bring me her unwanted boogie board. She was not happy that we had to head home, but once I explained I needed to go to the hospital, she instantly went and retrieved her older brother from the surf.

Within an hour, I was at Royal North Shore Hospital. I was very angry about being sick and told Brett not to tell anyone I was in hospital. They took blood; my troponin was ninety, not super alarming but not OK either. As I had to wait for another blood test, Brett headed home to feed the kids and put them to bed. I was feeling perfectly fine, relaxed even. My girlfriend, Kath, came to keep me company. They gave me a bed in A&E and hooked me up to an ECG. There didn't seem to be anything unusual with my heart rate.

At 9:50pm, the tightness returned but this time it was pain, real pain and it came fast. It was right in the middle of my chest. I was squeezing Kath's hand, and I asked her to call Brett to come back to the hospital. The pain got worse; they were giving me morphine but it made no difference. Brett had arrived and he too was holding my other hand. I could see the look on both their faces and I knew I was in trouble. Brett and Kath were there when I delivered my babies drug free; they had cared for me when I had meningitis; they both knew I had a high pain threshold so they knew this was serious. I would rather give birth three times over than experience that pain again.

The medical team really didn't know what was wrong with me. The pain lasted fifty minutes – I counted every minute. After much deliberation, the medical team decided on an angiogram. The angiogram was painful as my tolerance levels were super low. The angiogram shed no light on the situation. They admitted me and diagnosed me with Myopericarditis. I had to ask him to spell it so I could write it down. They administered anti biotics.

My devoted girlfriend and personal GP, Kath, was not satisfied with this diagnosis; she kept saying to me that the pain was far too much for it to be a symptom of Myopericarditis. I mentioned this to one of the doctors but he dismissed it and said everyone has different pain thresholds.

Finally, after an MRI, the SCAD was diagnosed, in the left descending artery. The first day, I cried and cried. My uncle had recently had a descending aortic dissection; he had to semi-retire immediately and completely change his lifestyle. I was scared that my life too was going to dramatically change forever. I was looking forward to taking on extra responsibility in my work role and now I thought my future employment and lifestyle quality was going to dramatically decrease – was not going to be good. My thoughts went to very unhelpful places.

I googled SCAD and discovered that SCAD sufferers, or really 'survivors', went on to do amazing things like run marathons and complete ocean swims. This information gave me hope and my motivation to share my story with you, so that you too can have hope as a SCAD survivor.

Sue North – 8th May 2016 – Aged 58

"No, not you of all people!" was the general response from my family and friends when they were told that I had just had a heart attack. Eight months later, it is still hard to believe that it happened, just 'out of the blue', with no warning signs whatsoever.

I was 58 years old at the time and have always had a healthy lifestyle, e.g., non-smoker, healthy diet, slim, only the occasional amount of alcohol. I practised yoga and walked, daily.

I have had high blood pressure for a number of years, but that was controlled with medication.

Last year (2016), on Mother's Day, we went for a picnic at the beach. It was cold and windy, but still lovely, sitting by the ocean. After lunch, we had a coffee at the café – I had a large mug. We then had a really long, beautiful walk along the beach and I will never forget that, I had just commented about how therapeutic it was, when I had a strange sensation in my throat. We were walking back to the car and into the strong headwind and I presumed that it must have been the cold air. I wrapped my scarf around my mouth and thought that I would feel better once I was back in the car. However, the feeling continued and I had slight tightness around my collarbones. I had no other symptoms and my husband thought it might have been my lungs and suggested I try a puff of his Ventolin that he uses for asthma.

I didn't feel ill at all, I just had mild discomfort, but instinct must have kicked in, as I decided to phone the Health Direct line for advice. I really thought I might be wasting their time but was advised to get to hospital as quickly as possible, as the nurse stated that he thought it was an angina attack.

It was then that I was diagnosed with SCAD, after having an angiogram.

I was fortunate that it was a small tear and that I had no further treatment, apart from being put on various medications. I was discharged after two nights and, shortly afterwards, attended rehabilitation talks and a number of Cardiac Rehabilitation sessions at the gym. I found these really beneficial and reassuring.

There were a couple of factors that I think may have contributed to having the SCAD. The first is that I had forgotten to take my blood pressure tablet that morning. Also, I had drunk a very large mug of caffeinated coffee and then embarked on a really long walk.

Since then, I NEVER forget my tablets and I have also given up caffeine, I now stick to drinking organic decaf tea and coffee. This helps with my blood pressure.

It is a huge shock, experiencing something like this, but I have found having support from others is a huge help. Also, with time, I feel I have gained a certain sense of acceptance. Initially, I did get sharp, stabbing-like pains quite regularly but was reassured by my wonderful cardiologist that it is muscular. I still get them occasionally, when I have overexerted myself, but take it as a message from my body to take it easy.

Once it has happened, I think you are always mindful about the possibility of it happening again. However, I feel reassured, being aware of the condition now, having medications to help and also the knowledge that I should seek medical attention, if I am in any doubt whatsoever. Because of these factors, I am in a much better position and feel positive about the future. I really appreciate every day now and am determined to get on with life (as long as I am carrying my spray!).

I am doing 'Zumba Gold' classes each week, which I love, and have also resumed daily walking and modified yoga.

My husband and I are off to our son's wedding in Holland this year and we are then going to travel to Spain, Portugal and England. There is a lot to look forward to.

I wish you luck with your recovery and SCAD journey and remember, never feel that you are alone, there is always someone to reach out to.

The Australian SCAD Survivors group, started by Pam McKenzie, has been a huge help and wonderful comfort to so many of us.

Susan Blanch – 1st January 2017 – Aged 35

I recently survived a SCAD Heart Attack. For this, there were no known risk factors or symptoms leading up to it. One minute I was there happily with my children, the next I was lucky to be alive.

New Year's Day, 2017. I woke up feeling great and rang a few family members and friends to wish them all the best for the New Year. Then I got up to prepare breakfast for the children – we were planning on going out to a party a bit later, so mood in the house was great. Next thing I know, I'm bent over in the kitchen, feeling like I have been kicked in the chest and struggling for breath. I started to feel very weak and shaky and like I wanted to be sick.

At this point, I'm wondering what on earth is going on – I know something is wrong, very wrong, but as I was fit, slim, healthy, and young, there was no way I could be having a heart attack, right? Yes, I have been under a lot of stress lately, but surely, it's just a bad asthma attack or some indigestion or something. I ask my 12-year-old daughter to please bring me my puffer (I do sometimes suffer from asthma), but this did absolutely nothing. She was wanting to ring the ambulance at this point, but I delay momentarily to ask her to ring 'Grandma' first. First thoughts were, if I have to go in, someone has to be here to look after the children.

By this time, my daughter had looked up all my symptoms – by then, I was also pale and sweating and had to sit, as I no longer had the strength to stand. "Mum you are having a heart

23

attack and I'm ringing 000 now and Grandma's coming." Great, by that point, I wanted them there NOW.

The ambulance arrived about half an hour later, as we live out of town, so my mum and a close friend arrived just before them. GTN spray given straight away, the ECG was very evident for a heart attack, but there was no mobile coverage for them to ring back to base.

I was loaded up into the back of the ambulance and we started our trip back to town, with my friend following behind. I remember stopping on the side of the road (I was later told it was for 20 minutes), I remember hearing the ambulance officer who was in the back with me asking for assistance from the one who was driving. I heard, "Is she conscious, she's gone into VF?" I remember feeling like I did not have the energy to respond to them and them stripping me. IV line in, injection, defib pads on my chest.

Next thing, we arrive at emergency. They wheeled me in, in only my underpants; luckily, someone had covered me with a sheet. I had no other clothes or belongings with me, as I hadn't been able to pack. I was still half expecting them to tell me I was wasting their time and it was a panic attack or something – anything – and I could just go on home.

No, the emergency staff confirmed that I had a heart attack and would not allow me to eat or drink anything, even though by this time, I was nauseous as I hadn't eaten anything since the night before.

The Life Flight helicopter was called in to fly me to a larger hospital a couple of hours away. Great, only helicopter I have ever been in, and I can't really remember any of it, as I slept most of the trip. If I'm going to have a flight booked and a holiday in another city, I want to enjoy it. Instead, I was strapped down to the bed, so I couldn't even see out of the windows – oh what a waste.

On arriving, the doctor who admitted me to the CCU asked me how I felt during the attack. I told him that I had felt like I was dying – he looked down at my admittance scans and told me very matter of factly, "Well, you were!" Bit of a shock to the system to be told that! I was still in shock and denial, and in a city, hours away from any friends or family, with not so much as a pair of knickers or a tooth brush with me. Luckily, the lovely nurses dressed me in one of the delightful, air-conditioned hospital gowns and found a new toothbrush for me.

My stay was made nicer by my lovely 'tea man' who would sneak extra milo into my drink for me, then stay and have a quick chat while I drank it.

Due to the public holidays, I had to wait for the angiogram. I was the baby in the CCU, with everyone else about twice my age. A couple of nurses told me that I really scared them. Me? How? I'm the least scariest person ever. Apparently, they are quite used to dealing with heart attacks in older people, but with me being their age made them realise it can happen to anyone.

The angiogram confirmed SCAD. The angiogram itself was quite traumatic for me, as I have very small wrists, it was decided that there was no way they could go in through them, so they had to go in through my groin. Afterwards I had two chatty male nurses leaning on my groin to keep the pressure on the area, so it didn't bleed – at that point, you don't care who is doing what.

Back down to recover in the ward and I had to lay completely flat for so long, before I would be allowed to come up to a 5% tilt, then 10% and so forth. However, only got to 10% and by this time was desperate to go to the toilet – ah, the joys of bed pans. Unfortunately, the slight sideways movement was enough to re-start-up bleeding from the groin, so back to being pressed on and iced. Then told I had to lay flat for a full 24 hours. Found out it is very hard to eat or drink flat with two arms that can't really bend due to the tubes in both of them.

I found it difficult emotionally when I was told I had SCAD, all the nurses told me, "That's great news, it wasn't a regular heart attack." I asked them how was it great, what caused it and how could I stop it happening again. I asked them if it was a regular attack, what would I do in order to prevent another attack. I was told that would be "eat healthy, keep blood pressure and cholesterol in check". Yes, however, what can I do to prevent another attack.

"OHH we don't know, as we don't know what causes it or how to prevent it."

"Exactly."

"Oh, we hadn't thought of it that way."

I think that is one of the scary things about SCAD. There are still so many unknowns. WHY? Why did it happen, and what can I do so it doesn't happen again. That is why I am so thankful to Pamela McKenzie, for organising this information and extra research into SCAD.

I was very relieved to be let out of hospital and thankful to my friends and family for coming into my home to help me look after my children and home.

Unfortunately, I was treated to another CCU holiday in May, but since then, I have been improving.

I just know that I have to take things slowly, listen to my body and rest when I need to.

Although I have been healing well from this experience, it changes who you are. Your expectations change, your values change, the way you look at life and life experiences change. Life is not taken for granted, nor are joys undervalued. Each day is valued for what it is. I am very aware that within our own lives, so much is beyond our control. I know I am very lucky to be here.

This has had the effect of making me much more relaxed and willing to 'go with the flow'. I know what is important in life, I will hold those things close and let the rest go.

I know there is a reason I am still here. I know I want to use this life I have been given.

To all those who are going through a similar journey, take care of yourselves, give yourself time to heal, emotionally and physically. Yes, your life will be forever changed, but you will find your new you, and you will go on and find your new challenges and joys. Take care and enjoy it and know that we are all Survivors.

Tania Clark

Mother to five children, aged 22–20 and twins. In recent years, I found a love of exercise and began my days with an hour at the gym alternating cardio and weights. I also began running but only short runs of several kilometres. Although I felt tired, I had no health concerns.

Several weeks prior to my SCAD, I had a very stressful time. With regard to one of my children, this was a very difficult time.

One weekend away, camping with my husband, I experienced chest pains during the night. In hindsight, I now think I had a dissection that night. The pain was similar to that which I experienced two weeks later, although not as severe. The following weeks, I felt very fatigued and I barely attended the gym and left in disgust when I couldn't complete my program. Two weeks later, I attempted to do a short run but found it too difficult; no chest pain, just fatigue. Later that morning, I began to feel unwell and took myself to the local medical centre and had an ECG which showed nothing abnormal. Later that day, I experienced chest pain. A blood test showed elevated troponin levels. Fortunately, my own GP was on duty and was vaguely aware of SCAD. Later that night, I was transported to Monash Medical Centre, Clayton. Upon arrival, an angiogram showed several arteries had dissected. The drug-eluting stents were positioned in my right coronary artery (RCA).

When I arrived in the CCU, I developed ventricular fibrillation arrest and was cardioverted to sinus rhythm twice. Following this, I was taken to the Cardiac Theatre for triple bypass surgery (LIMA, SVG OM2, SVG PDA).

Ten days in ICU and six weeks of recovery and rehab in hospital and I came home, eager to get my life back on track. I attended the local cardiac rehab sessions a few times but they weren't aimed at a SCAD survivor. Gradually, I increased my daily walks and I felt my strength returning.

When I was discharged from the hospital, I was taking Clopidogrel, Bisoprolol and Lovastatin. After consulting with my cardiologist, I have discontinued taking all medication;

27

although my new cardiologist wants me to resume taking Ramipril and Bisoprolol. I will consider this after the results of my yearly echo.

Jessica Blair

As I have a C3 to C6 spinal cord injury and use a wheelchair, I have Autonomic Dysreflexia and do not experience much pain below C3–C4.

As I do not experience pain in the same way, slight pains (if I had actually felt them) in my chest and left arm were thought to be nothing more than indigestion or muscle strain.

On Thursday, 25th May 2017, I went into St Vincent's Hospital for a pre-admission clinic for a total hip replacement. Things were not as they usually were as during the proceedings, it was discovered that, unbeknownst to me or Andrew, I had recently had two small heart attacks. These were discovered by an ECG at the pre-admission examination.

On Friday, 2nd June 2017, I went to NSW Cardiology to see Dr Andrew Jabbour for an EEG cardiac ultrasound. Then, on Monday, 5th June 2017, I went to St Vincent's Hospital for a CT angiogram which confirmed that a serious cardiac event had taken place. I left as soon as I had dressed after the CT angiogram, even though the Cardiac Specialist wanted me to be admitted to the hospital. Later that evening, we received a phone call from Dr Jabbour telling me that I had a very serious condition and he was arranging for me to have an angiogram the next morning.

The following morning, during the angiogram, I suffered a significant hypotensive bradycardic episode which truncated the proceedings, though enough information was gathered to make a diagnosis. Afterwards, they admitted me to the Coronary Care Unit.

Wednesday, when my husband, Andrew, arrived he was surprised to find me drinking coffee and moving around the ward in my wheel chair. Andrew had gone to the dental hospital to have some new dentures fitted and was intending to meet me at the hospital afterwards with my nightwear and some other items I needed. At about 2pm, part of my medical team came into my ward and explained that they were getting me ready to either insert a stent or perform a bypass operation. Then at about 2:30pm, another part of my medical team came into my ward and explained that I was being discharged and that I should get ready to go home.

I was given instructions upon my discharge that if I felt any chest pain, I was to call an ambulance. "Ha," since I do not experience pain in the same way as everyone else. How am I to know when to call an ambulance? That is why I threw those instructions away.

All of my medications stay the same as the doctors' consensus was that my SCAD should be managed conservatively.

Apparently, my SCAD was totally asymptomatic as I cannot quite recall when it happened and I do not recall any symptoms at all.

On Thursday, 8th of June, I went back to a normal life, six or eight hours full on flat out. On Friday, 23rd of June, I did an 11-hour day with wood-turner friends at the 'Working with Wood Show' 2017.

Coralie Maloney – 8th February 2017 – Aged 41

The year 2017 started off as a great year personally and professionally. My oldest son, James, who is all grown up, just turned five and was very much looking forward to starting school on 30th January and our little Peter, who was only 2½ years old but so full of energy and character, was embarking on a new year in the preschool room at Montessori with the three- and four-year-olds which was a big deal for him too.

My husband, Joseph, and I had been looking to buy a home for our little family. My career was taking off and my role as a Marketing and Business Development Manager was gaining a lot of momentum as the company I was working for was growing at great speed. So, whilst exciting, it was busy – very busy – but no more stressful than the norm of a small family and just as busy as a family with young, boisterous, busy boys! We were not different and pretty happy.

Whilst being moderately fit, maintaining good cholesterol and good diet, and also having worked in the fitness industry as a personal trainer and fitness instructor, having a heart attack was something that I could have put money on; it could not happen to me.

Wednesday, 8th February 2017, was a normal day. Joseph headed to work before 8am. I got myself and our boys ready, dropped them off at school and Montessori, and headed to work. Around 10:30am after wolfing down my morning coffee and morning tea, I was talking with my colleague, Lorrie, when I started to feel a burning sensation in the middle of my chest over my sternum; the same feeling that you have when you've swallowed a tablet without enough water. It wasn't painful to begin with but annoying. I just thought it was indigestion and continued my conversation. After a couple of minutes, I told Lorrie the sensation is really not going away and I couldn't manage to keep talking and thought that I might get a big glass of water. After a few more minutes, the pain started to become quite uncomfortable but I then just assumed it was anxiety from the indigestion pain that seemed to progress. I thought I would just go somewhere quiet and relax, but the pain got worse. I, still at this point, thought it was nothing. It did not cross my mind once that something was happening to my heart even after years of administering first aid in the gym. My colleagues kept checking on me, but I still didn't think it was anything bad. After around 25 minutes with the pain still there and escalating, all of a sudden, my left arm felt heavy and weak. Right then, I knew something was not good. I carefully got up and walked to get help. All of a sudden, I felt the urge to fall to the floor but managed to alert my friends to call an ambulance as I thought something was really bad. Ambulance arrived within a couple of minutes and hooked me up to an ECG; my heart rate was only 45bpm and was unstable, and with my background, I knew that was bad. Thankfully, that period settled but the pain did not. I was given Aspirin and a spray of GTN which did not alleviate the pain. I was told I was going to hospital because something wasn't right in my heart. As we sped off in the ambulance with sirens going, I was pretty scared. All I could think about was my boys, my babies, but I knew I had to stay calm and keep my heart rate down. I had another spray of GTN which still didn't alleviate the pain, and the paramedic was reassuring me how far things have come with the heart surgery and that they can now unblock an artery with just a catheter in my wrist. Hang on… what did you say? My thoughts were, *What the hell is happening?*

Joseph, my husband, was working at the RAH and met me as I arrived by ambulance and at this point, I was given another spray of GTN but my pain was still an 8 out of 10. I was rushed straight in for an angiogram and was told afterwards that I'd had a Spontaneous Coronary Artery

Dissection. I googled (as you do) on my phone, but still was not aware I'd also had a heart attack. I didn't need a stent and recovered well with antiplatelet medication and blood thinners. It wasn't until the cardiologist did ward rounds the following morning that he informed me that I'd had a heart attack. His words were: 'not an old man's heart attack but a heart attack just the same'. I was in complete shock.

On Thursday evening, around 11pm, I started to feel the burning sensation in my chest again, but was told that it's probably just indigestion. It didn't go away so I buzzed the nurse again, and he did an ECG but no changes were visible. You never forget those physical memories with trauma and I knew the pain was the same, and I also thought how can I have indigestion, I hadn't eaten for five hours! I went to sleep with reservation and was a little scared. I woke in the morning and the pain was right there – I knew it! ECG showed changes and GTN didn't alleviate the pain. I went down immediately for another angiogram which showed the original artery that dissected had closed over. Hello heart attack #2 in two days! It settled with further medication. I was scared at this point; I had always been fit and healthy, and considered myself a young 41-year-old and was not ready to take a back seat, but that is what had to happen.

The following day, I got up in the morning and went to use the bathroom, and the nurse came rushing in and asked me if I was OK. I was fine but she told me to look at the monitor and my heart machine was flashing, and my heart rate was around 160bpm! Turns out, my body was so freaked out by my last three days, it was obviously not reacting well and I started Beta-blockers for three days before we could get my resting heart rate under 80bpm.

Whilst I felt OK coming home, I was petrified being around my sons, they were so busy and boisterous. I remember the week after I got home I knelt down to the ground and Peter took a hanger off my back like an AFL player. He was two, he didn't understand. It took quite a while to adjust but we got there.

My thyroid took a hit too from the stress of the ordeal and now I am on Thyroxine. Continued chest pain was also further investigated and I was found to have Microvascular Dysfunction (spasming of the microvascular arteries) and have started new medication for this too. After four months, I am starting to feel OK, but need to take it easy for another 12 months.

I am so thankful to my wonderful husband for his support and love, and care of the boys during this time; it hasn't been easy for him either. I am also thankful to my amazing friends and family who supported us and also to my wonderful boss, Sam, who has been so supportive of me easing back to work.

Jo Coombes – Aged 51

"I'm leaving on a leer jet, don't know when I'll be back again." That was kind of how it all started; being whisked off my tropical island adopted home of Vanuatu to Brisbane on my own personal leer jet. Well, I wasn't entirely alone, I had an intensive care specialist doctor, a nurse and my partner along for the ride. My most vivid memory of the jet is being given jelly snake lollies and thinking it was pretty cool to clear customs by the side of the plane.

As I write this, I am approaching the 5th anniversary of my SCAD.

My SCAD happened while living at the time in the South Pacific country of Vanuatu. I had met a friend for a cocktail at my favourite tropical island resort, and came home to start dyeing some silk. I'm a fashion designer and textile artist. I was 51 at the time; a bit stressed with deadlines but otherwise fit and healthy.

The first moment I knew something was wrong was when I went to lift some silk out of a bucket of water – a couple of metres of silk is very light even when wet – but I could not lift it. Trying to raise my arms felt like I was trying to lift a bag of cement rather than a few metres of silk fabric.

I wandered around my garden for a while feeling very unwell – heavy chest, dizziness, numbness in my arms – when my jaw started to feel tingly. Then as though there were small explosions happening within my jawbone, I knew I was in trouble. I mentioned to my partner that I didn't feel well and said, "No problem, but just in case you need to know at some point, this is what my symptoms are." He immediately called an ambulance.

Our fabulous community-funded, private ambulance took me to a small clinic where I was injected with blood thinners and stayed overnight while my troponin levels were checked.

The following evening, a leer jet arrived from Australia (thank goodness for Medevac insurance). An intensive care doctor and nurse from Australia transferred me to the leer jet for a flight to Brisbane.

On arrival in Brisbane, I was put into another ambulance for the trip to hospital; up until then, I had been feeling OK. I was concerned and somewhat embarrassed this might be a big fuss about nothing. Suddenly, I could feel myself falling deeper and deeper, and stopped breathing.

I arrived in Brisbane in the early hours of Saturday morning and had to wait until Monday for a specialised angiogram and IVUS which diagnosed my SCAD.

Five years before my SCAD, I'd had my thyroid removed due to thyroid cancer. I felt I could cope with one major issue as part of my medical history ... but with a medical history of thyroid cancer and now a cardiac issue, along with a treatment regime of six tablets a day, sometimes I wondered if I would ever feel 'normal' again.

There were times in the days, weeks and months following my SCAD that I despaired; I was used to doing fairly physical work as a designer and textile artist. Moving heavy racks of clothing and throwing around bolts of cloth were just part of what I did pre SCAD.

At the time of my SCAD, there were less than 100 members on the US-based international SCAD survivors Facebook page, now there are over 1800, and only a handful of known Australian survivors.

Five years later, knowing what I know now, this is the advice I would give my newly-diagnosed self.

Please be gentle with yourself. In hindsight, I am horrified at what I was doing in the months following my SCAD when I 'thought' I was being easy on myself. I should have done much less. Taken a slower pace to heal, both psychologically and physically. There is a temptation in those early days when you just want to get back to 'normal', to do what you have always done as though it is some kind of race against yourself. Don't fall for that temptation; give yourself a break.

Listen to your body; when the body is telling you it needs a break, stop. Your body is the best indicator of what it does and does not need, what it can and cannot cope with.

Take an active interest in your medical care. Don't presume the people treating you have all or... any answers. If your first cardiologist doesn't 'believe' in SCAD, find a new one.

Connect with others who know what you are going through. Issues come up that might be hard to talk about with friends and loved ones. It helps to connect with others who have had a similar experience. There were times when I regularly had thoughts that I was about to have another SCAD that would be fatal. This is not something I felt comfortable talking to my loved ones about; it was helpful to have a few SCAD sisters online who I could talk to. By the way, five years later, those thoughts occur less and less often now.

The advice following a regular heart attack is focussed on health promotion strategies of diet and exercise. This tends to be part of the package of advice for SCAD survivors also, even though we know that the majority of SCAD cases are people who generally have an exemplary history of diet and exercise.

Personally, I'm no longer interested in pushing my body to its limits. I know it has limits and would rather just keep it ticking over till I no longer need it.

If I want four coffees a day and it does not cause me heart palpitations, if it makes me happy, I do it.

I was a fit and healthy 41-year-old and an active mum of two children aged three and seven at the time of my SCAD. I had always been very energetic and enjoyed sports, travelling, running, swimming, kayaking and camping. I lived a very 'outdoorsy' lifestyle. I had just returned from a fantastic overseas holiday in Bali with my family and friends when twenty-four hours later my world changed forever.

I was at an 'open for inspection', viewing a house that we were about to buy when apparently, I felt as though I was going to faint and had a pain in my arm (I don't have any memory about the day or a couple of weeks either side of my SCAD). My husband arrived late to the inspection, so by the time he arrived, he found me in the backyard not feeling very well. I had broken out in a sweat, had a pain or numbing feeling in my left arm and thought that I may faint. All of these symptoms were quite mild and I was still upright and talking at this stage. My husband thought something wasn't right and wanted to call an ambulance, but I didn't feel that bad and definitely didn't want to cause a scene in front of people I didn't know. I didn't want to embarrass myself or put anyone out, so said that I would go to a doctor instead. I just wanted out of the house quietly!

Thankfully, my husband and the real estate agent ignored my request for no ambulance and called one anyway. The ambulance arrived to assess me and within a few minutes of their arrival, I went into cardiac arrest in front of them. No pulse and no heartbeat! This, of course, was so sudden and absolutely not to be expected – I was a fit and healthy person.

The paramedics called for back-up and I had several people working on me for quite some time. I had someone pumping air into my lungs, someone administering drugs and several people taking turns in pumping my chest. I had CPR for over half an hour and seven defibrillation shocks before finally getting some sort of heart rhythm back. Half an hour is a long time without a pulse, so no one was really sure if I would pull through and if I did pull through, the extent of brain damage I may or may not have.

I was rushed to St Vincent's hospital in Sydney, and urgently taken to the cath lab where it was discovered I had suffered a SCAD and my LAD artery had dissected from top to bottom and was hundred percent occluded. Three stents were placed in my heart to help re-open my artery and I was placed in an induced coma. During this time in ICU, my body was chilled to help reduce swelling and damage to my brain. I was hooked up to several machines and I had a small balloon placed in my heart to help it beat. It was really a very frightening and critical time over the next 24–48 hours. Discussions were made amongst my family trying to decide if my children should be brought in to say their goodbyes to me or not. Thankfully, due to the amazing care I received at hospital and some kind of miracle, I pulled through!

Liza Stearn – 29 September – Aged 41

After a week in ICU, I was transferred to the cardiac care unit and on this day, I had yet another heart attack. I remember parts of this heart attack and the numbness I felt in my arm and one of the nurses advising me I was having a full STEMI.

My recovery was a long and slow process, I spent a total of six weeks in hospital. Whilst recovering, I had a few little hiccups along the way. I had bacterial pneumonia which meant I spent days and days feeling terrible and coughing up bright red blood, a blood clot in my jugular vein where my PIC line was inserted and several little blood clots in my leg to name a few. A few days before I was released from hospital, I had another operation to insert an internal cardiac defibrillator (ICD) into my chest and heart, just in case I was to ever have another cardiac arrest. During this time, I also learnt that I have FMD (fibromuscular dysplasia) which is quite common amongst other SCAD victims.

The first six months after my SCAD and SCA was a very draining and scary time in my life. I was exhausted 95% of the time; my body was adjusting to a cocktail of drugs. I was in pain from the broken ribs and ICD. I was unable to drive and walking was a real effort. It was also a very emotional and nerve-racking time in my life. Each little twinge or pain I had in my chest, I thought I could be having another heart attack and going to bed each night, I would hope and pray that I wouldn't die in my sleep and leave my kids without a mum.

I was one of the lucky ones to survive and am extremely fortunate that I had so much help, time and support with my recovery. My family and friends were really amazing and dedicated months and months to caring and looking after me; something I'll never be able to thank them for enough.

I am glad to say now that I am a couple of years out from my SCAD and I have adjusted to the new version of me. It's sometimes hard to say goodbye to the old me, but I have to be extremely grateful and thankful that I am still here and for what I have today.

Life is good and I plan on making the most of it for as long as I can!

Louise Gardner – 9th August 2017 – Aged 47

My name is Louise Gardner and I was only 47 when I had my SCAD, only a few weeks ago. It came as a complete shock, something I would never have imagined would happen to me, mostly because I had absolutely no warning signs at all and I was going about my day as I always did on a Wednesday.

I was, however, born with SVT (Supra Ventricular Tachycardia). I used to mention it to my GP all the time that I had this weird thing with my heart where it would race for about half an hour regularly, make me feel sick to the point I had to lie down, I couldn't drive, but she would say don't worry about it, so I didn't. It wasn't until I was about 18 weeks pregnant with my second son when my heart went into Tachycardia and after 45 minutes or so, it still hadn't stopped, so I became a bit worried, rang my obstetrician and he very calmly, as they do, said, "Oh, could you come in and I'll have a look."

But I said, "Well, I'm a bit busy at the moment, I have my friend over for morning tea and we are having scones."

My doctor said, "Just let your friend know she will need to go home and I need you to come in."

I wasn't very impressed but I drove myself into Busselton from Dunsborough with my 12-month-old in tow. After a phone call to a physician in Perth, they discovered my SVT, which was kind of good, because at least I knew what was wrong now and we could treat it. Of course, I couldn't have surgery until my baby was born, so in May 2006, I had an electrophysiology study done, which is keyhole surgery through the groin to have an ablation. That worked an absolute treat and I couldn't be happier having a normal heartbeat, it was just the best feeling until exactly three years later to the date, my heart started playing up again. I was then diagnosed with AVE (Atrial Ventricular Ectopic) heartbeat. Great, just great – not.

The day I had my SCAD episode was my normal busy Wednesday where I have to cram in a lot of stuff before I work the next two days, so I did my 6-km walk, as I have done for about 16 years now, went to Coles to do my food shopping, then I stopped in at the post office to collect a parcel when the excruciating pain hit me like a tonne of bricks out of the blue. It took my breath away and my back was pulsating with a different pain. I do remember thinking, *Oh no, this is not good and I probably should ask that lady to call me an ambulance,* but then I remembered I had nearly $500 worth of food shopping in my car, so I'd better get that home and into the fridge first, thinking hopefully the pain will go away then, not realising in a million years I was having a heart attack.

So off I went, drove myself home, lugged all my food shopping up to the house, safely packed away all the fridge and freezer stuff before thinking, *Oh no, it's still really painful, I'd better get myself to the GP and have him check it out.* So off I go again, driving the 15 minutes to my GP, who then said, "You need to go to Busselton Emergency."

And I said, "Oh, there is no way I can drive to Busselton, it's just too far, I don't think I'll make it, I've only just made it here from my house."

To which he replied "Oh, you're not driving anywhere, I'm calling you an ambulance."

I said, "No, don't bother them, ring my husband and he'll come and get me." Anyway, the amazing ambulance crew came to collect me and off to Busselton Emergency I go for a few hours while they try to work out what's wrong with me.

They couldn't, so they rang my Heart Specialist in Perth and he said get her to Bunbury or Perth, and I'm like, "What the heck, I haven't got time for this, I'm really busy and need to get home and get my jobs done." Plus I didn't want to miss

The Bold and The Beautiful at 4:30pm. I became quite distressed and the nurse said, "It's time now for you to ring somebody to let them know what's happening." And I just couldn't speak to anyone, so I asked them to get a dear friend of mine who works at the hospital to come and see me, so she rang my husband and my boss to let him know I wouldn't be at work the next day – oh and to also take my keys and get my car from my GP's carpark because it had a cooked chook still in it and that was dinner that night. So, when I was being transferred to Bunbury, I politely told the driver he had one hour to get me there before my show started and he delivered me with ten minutes to spare. I was super impressed. So, into CCU (Coronary Care Unit) I go for the next four days. Even the nursing staff were very accommodating. They left me to watch my show in peace. What more could I ask for except for more pain relief.

My diagnosis was taking some time and I was starting to get worried. On the Thursday, they did an Echo (ultrasound) and found nothing untoward, so I thought, *Awesome, I can go home then*, and of course the answer was, "No, we'll do an angiogram on you tomorrow."

And I said, "Oh no, that's okay, I don't really feel like one of those, thanks." But they came at the crack of dawn the next day to give me one anyway. It was so good, I don't remember anything except for the Cardiologist being a bit excited at what she had discovered and explained it to me. Interesting.

At first, I felt really hard done by, this is so inconvenient, it's interrupting my life, I already had an annoying heartbeat that nobody seems to be able to do anything with anyway, what makes anyone think I need this other ridiculous rare heart condition. I will be getting behind in my housework and I can't go to work, so I'm not getting paid, which means my sons' school fees aren't getting paid, but on the other hand, I was soooooooo grateful to be alive, because I understand not everyone survives this. Then your mind just gets away with all sorts of thoughts and I shed a lot of tears whilst laying in hospital for four days. I lost my confidence, especially when

I was told I wasn't allowed to drive or go to work for two weeks. I felt like my life as I knew it was over. How was someone so energetic and busy like myself going to cope with sitting on the couch for two weeks, not being able to do a thing. It worked for about five days but after going through the torment of watching my husband and sons do MY jobs, it just all got too much, so I started doing them again myself, but very slowly and carefully.

My poor husband was really shocked but thankful I was still alive. My sons were very out of sorts until I was discharged from hospital. Once I was home, everything seemed to click back into place for them. For me, it has changed me a lot in the way I think, I don't seem to care so much as I did with certain things. I'm still very particular and sweat the small stuff with my housework, but that's my nature, but other things like, for example, I have been wanting security screens on my front door, only for three years, well, I am getting them done now and not waiting, because I can't guarantee how long I'm here for and I want to enjoy what I have sacrificed and worked so hard for my whole life. Like the saying goes, you can't take it with you.

Surrounding yourself with people who genuinely care about you and avoiding the ones that don't is important for your recovery, because life is just too short, as you have now learned, to put up with any nonsense anymore. Go with the flow, you will have your down days and up days, don't fight the down days, just go with them, but teach yourself to be more mindful with your thoughts. As soon as you start having negative thoughts, turn them around into positive ones. Most importantly, listen to your body, it will tell you when it's time to slow down and have a rest.

Lee Harper – 13th July 2017 – Aged 53

I'm 53, female and live in Christchurch, New Zealand. My partner and I are from Tasmania. I was born in Victoria. My partner was offered a job at a structural engineering firm, working as part of the rebuild of Christchurch after the devastating earthquakes in 2010 and 2011. He moved to Christchurch the day after our first grandchild was born in Tasmania in June 2013. I stayed in Tasmania and moved to Christchurch in November 2014, 18 months after my partner. I left behind our family, had our 20-year-old dog put to sleep, left my job which I really enjoyed, rented out the family home and said goodbye to friends.

I work in Community Engagement, Communications and Construction, but finding ongoing permanent work in Christchurch has been challenging. Christchurch values volunteering, so following my passion, I volunteer as a sewing/quilter at the Women's Prison. There are about six ladies who visit the 'Self-Care' unit one night each week. We assist and guide the inmates in making sewn items for their babies, children and loved ones. Items like quilts, cushions and aprons. The Self-Care unit also houses the Mother and Babies Unit. I love this role and am extremely passionate about our commitment to these young women.

My heart attack commenced whilst travelling from my new job (of only four days) to volunteering at the rural-based prison. I had stopped on the side of the road about 1.5km away to have a bite to eat and a drink. It had been raining heavily over the last few days. The car slid and became bogged. At that moment, I had an immediate sense of anxiety, as I knew I couldn't be late. My chest began to tighten with waves of pain, which I dismissed. I got out of the car to check to see where the wheels were located so I could work out where to place the steering wheel, I thought if I didn't get the car out, I was unable to walk the 1km to the nearest farm house. Remarkably, in one move of the steering wheel and a fistful of accelerator, the car came out of the quagmire and back onto the road.

Arriving at the prison in time to meet my colleagues, I recounted the 'bogged' story. I mentioned that I still 'felt' incredibly tense and needed to catch my breath. Having already cleared prison security, I sat down, sweating profusely and feeling pain in my chest. People were talking to me, but I couldn't hear what they were saying. The pain became intense, travelled to my back and down my left arm. The prison service has a nurse on site (who took my BP) and a first responder. My BP was high and the decision to call an ambulance was made. This all happened in a matter of minutes. The paramedics arrived in ten mins, made their assessments, determined the likelihood of an inferior STEMI, heart attack, and transported me the 25kms to Christchurch Hospital.

I'm incredible thankful for their quick actions.

In the ambulance, the paramedics were in constant phone discussions with other medical staff, I'm not even sure what they were talking about, it was all 'numbers and elevations' jumbled, like code. In response and with some slight amusement, I asked the paramedic if I was going to die. He laughed along with me and said he hoped not, not on his watch, too much paper work for him, "but we are in a bit of a rush to get you straight to hospital where the team are waiting for us".

"So, they know I'm having a heart attack?" I asked.

"Yes, they do, and there is a doctor following us in that car behind us (pointing)."

"Oh," I said, "the one that has its lights flashing?"

"Yes," he responded.

I remembered thinking that, *This is my 'life-changing moment',* the one that you hear other people talk about. I laid there thinking about what I could change in my life, I had this sneaky excitement, the endless possibilities.

The truth be known, I was utilising a thinking strategy to deny what was happening.

Once in the ED, I was rushed into a bed location, people slapped monitor pads, took bloods, inserted cannulas, I was wired up with people asking questions. By now, my partner had arrived and then the biggest of the big doctor's talks happened. It was the CONSENT process. This was like a wound within itself, a big one at that, opening the reality of how unwell I was. This was a critical moment for me. I was consenting to the likelihood of the %s of risk associated with heart surgery. I was consenting to angiograms, stents, open-heart surgery, blood transfusions and any other heart procedures, basically if and whatever was required to fix the causation of the heart attack. It had an undertone of 'no guarantees'. I immediately said, "I'm not going to surgery unless I speak to my two sons." One lives in Sydney with his wife and our two grandchildren and the other in Tasmania. I spoke to them, told them I was having a heart attack, I was having surgery and that if anything happens, I want them to know I loved them all very, very much. It was incredible hard for them. I tried not to cry, but I did. One of them could hardly speak to me; fortunately, his partner is an RN, so I spoke to her as well. I wanted to talk to my sister, who is an RN as well, my only sibling, but she couldn't be contacted at that time.

Going into surgery, I was left with the memories of my family, thinking about the last time I had seen them all was when I had returned to Tasmania six months prior, as my mother had passed away on New Year's Day. I spent a month at home, sorting my mother's affairs along with my sister, and three weeks recovering from severe chest infection which had briefly landed me in hospital.

My partner accompanied me as far as the cath lab, I told him I loved him and we had a wee kiss goodbye. I was there for about 2.5 hours. I laid there, watching my heart on the monitors as they fed the dye through the various vessels. I was so cold, it was freezing in that room, I shook and shivered, whilst being entertained by *Pink Floyd* (The Wall or Darkside of the Moon or both) and good-humoured staff. The pain was agonising and exhausting, it was like the longest birthing 'contraction' in the entire world happening all in my chest. I was imploding from the inside out, I was a contradiction. I had been in severe pain since 5pm that evening. The pain killers had not shifted the pain. I was assured that once they found the problem, the pain would stop. And it did. They found the dissection in my Right Coronary Artery (RCA). They told me they were inserting a stent and that I would feel some further pain as they inflate the balloon and then relief once the stent is in place. This is exactly what happened. Everyone was happy with the outcome, but no more than me. The surgeon was checking the repair when I started to have severe pain again. I told them that the pain had returned. The surgeon had found the dissection had migrated and he inserted another two stents. The final repair was three stents covering 9cm length.

I was sent to the Acute Cardio ward, where my night was restless. I was still having significant chest and arm pain. Using pain medications, this dissipated by morning. I was too frightened to sleep, as I kept watching the monitors for any changes, the fear of what had happened had finally set in. I was genuinely frightened. I stayed in the hospital for four days. On leaving, my Echo showed my heart was normal and I had sustained no heart damage. The Cardio Nurse Educators visited me to talk about SCAD, what had happened, how it happens, what they had done and what the follow-up was going to be. In my case, I could drive in two weeks, that I could return to normal activities in 3–4 weeks. Also, I could go to Heart Physio Club, a group that meets to discuss topics, such as diet and medications. They also run a half-hour exercise circuit session and an opportunity to ask questions over a cup of tea and a bickie. I go, reluctantly, but I do attend. I'm the youngest heart patient there. I have learnt quite a bit about heart health since attending and recommend the opportunity to any new SCAD Patient.

I can't tell you what impact this has had on my children but I do know that they are grateful and have said how lucky that all went well with the surgery. My partner was there throughout, and he values the experience as one which has changed my life. He cares very deeply for me and does what he can to help where he knows how. We have been together since 1983.

The funny thing is, two weeks prior to this heart attack, I had been upset about not being able to find employment. I was tired and my anxiety levels were high. I found it difficult negotiating recruitment agencies, biased attitudes, employment laws and other associated hurdles in getting a job. From my experience, Christchurch is a difficult place for some outsiders to get employment. Most agencies are full of off-shore recruiters with an average age of 20 something. So, it is hard being recruited when you're a female, Australian and in your 50s. My experience says being Australian, you are not well received here in Christchurch, they are more likely to recruit fellow countrymen who are here in Christchurch for extended periods. It's a damaged city, not just structurally, the bricks and mortar, but huge psychological issues for many parts of the community. I've found workplaces to be unhealthy, perforated with bullying and unacceptable personal behaviours with a lack of understanding and resistance away from new OH&S statutes and a tardiness towards healthy Human Resource practices.

I'd said to my partner I was stressed, I felt my chest was going to explode, I felt that I was going to bleed out, that I was going to die here, I said I felt incredibly unwell. I could feel that my anxiety levels had increased to a point where I had seen the GP a few weeks earlier and he had prescribed AD. I felt nothing was improving or changing medically. It was just this overwhelming sense of doom that was infiltrating every part of my life. Nothing since moving to Christchurch had gone to plan. Get a job, find friends, blend into community. Parts of it had begun, but my sense of worth by not being employed long term was physically heartbreaking.

That week, we arranged a trip to Hamner Springs, home of The Hot Springs and Spas, for four days of Randr. I just wanted to relax. With the Friday and Monday off work, my partner and I with our wee dog, Ava, headed up to The Springs. In the middle of Hamner Springs, there is a little mountain called Conical Hill. On the Friday, we attempted to walk up to the top, but I couldn't keep up, I was puffed out every ten steps or so. I'd stop, regulate my breathing, wait for the pulse in my throat to subside and then edge a bit further up the hill. We made it. Jokingly, I kept saying to my partner "I'm going to die, LOL, I'm so unfit, what's wrong with me? They'll have to remove me with a helicopter." The banter went on and on, I even asked if there was a hospital at Hamner Springs.

The next day, with Ava, we walked about 8kms through the forest and back to the motel. We spent Sunday at the Spa. I had booked a full massage for us both. It was the worst massage I had ever had. Not because of the very talented masseur, but as I laid down on the bed, my chest felt swollen and uncomfortable, like I had bad indigestion. The feeling wouldn't shift. I couldn't get comfortable, I couldn't relax. Felt I had wasted a significant amount of money we really couldn't afford. I felt guilty.

Amongst all of this, there had been good news on the Friday on our way to Hamner Springs, I'd received a phone call telling me I had a short-term work contract. The first for the year (it was now July). This meant we needed to return to Christchurch for me to start the job on the Monday. I was at this new job for four days before the SCAD on the Thursday evening. I didn't return to the job, as it was a contract position.

I was unemployed again. But I was alive!

At the time of writing this, some nine weeks post-SCAD, it is too early to say anything has changed big time, it's more the subtleties of life. I am not afraid to say how it is. I'm honest about what I think and I can own it. I also walk away when I don't want to be involved. I don't want to be involved with people who smother me, who take ownership of my efforts and are negative.

What I did learn was that I had a much bigger friendship network here in NZ than what I realised. I also learnt that people that I have known most of my life were not there for support, not necessarily for me, but for my partner and sons. I felt sadness for them. One of the Cardio Rehab clinics I attend had a speaker who spoke about this scenario. He said people's reactions can be varied, for many reasons, and although we may feel disappointed in their lack of concern for us and our family, their reasons are private, where we may never know why. Some people just can't cope with the idea of near death, or sickness, maybe it is too close to their own situation, others don't know what to say, or may think they are expected to do something, and the minority, a very small minority just bury their heads in the sand because the situation is all too hard and it might go away. Some don't know what having a heart attack or SCAD means. Take any help and assistance you receive from everyone with open arms. I learnt new things about my Christchurch 'acquaintances', and now I can say we have better friendships from this experience.

For any new survivor, who reads this, I want to say that my life has changed. I just don't know how yet. Having touched on my thoughts about changing things in my life whilst in the ambulance, I recall lying on the table in cath lab at the most delinquent of moments, waiting for something to shift my new thinking into a higher gear, with my soul now opened, I was now ready to feel some warm fuzzy lightning bolt, a shazam, a poof, a bang! That lightbulb moment which I believed was now in my grasp!

Clearly, a grasp that was not needed, it just didn't happen and I've been amusingly disappointed ever since.

Change will come, but change will present itself, I'm not forcing change or making rushed decisions. I'm letting life be, I will be around for a good while and I'm now open to consider anything that comes my way.

Enjoy yourself and just be kind to others.

Helena King – Aged 50

I was fifty years old in June and we (husband and then eight-year-old son) went to America to celebrate my coming of age!

My background is nursing and I've worked in the health industry for thirty years. I have a group of four friends including myself who worked together long ago and we stayed in touch and probably caught up once or twice a year. One of them developed breast cancer in 2014. The same year, another one died suddenly from a heart attack six weeks post foot surgery. The third was diagnosed with lung cancer in October 2015 and died six weeks later on the 13th of November 2015, and I had my heart attack two weeks later on 1st December 2015.

Needless to say, it was a very stressful lead-up to my event. I worked permanent night shift at the time; 11pm to 8am, seven nights on, seven off and had done for seven years. This also placed a lot of stress on my body. Forty-eight hours prior to my event, I had an episode at work, where I felt weird, had a headache and expressive dysphasia (couldn't get my words out) for a few minutes. I went to the GP who decided it was a migraine – the first one I'd ever had. I felt fine the next few days and went to my aqua aerobics class. I was in the shower at the gym after the class and felt a sudden pain in my throat, like when you have that football-in-the-throat sensation; when you're going to cry, but worse. Then, I felt an explosive pain in the 'right' side of my chest and I knew something was seriously wrong. Without getting dressed (for fear I'd keel over in the shower), I opened the door and called for help. The life guard soon came and called the ambulance immediately. The pain had not subsided and I became short of breath.

When the paramedics arrived, they hooked me up to a three-lead ECG and I asked if I was I having a heart attack, and he said it looks like it! I was taken to Box Hill Hospital and required a couple of lots of morphine prior to arriving.

The pain in my chest then subsided but I had a lot of pain in my back. They did bloods and kept me monitored and did a CT angiogram thinking I'd had an aortic dissection. It came back OK, however, troponin and ECG changes did not. I was transferred to a private hospital later that day. Soon after I arrived, approximately eight hours after the first episode, I developed the exact same chest and throat pain and was taken for an urgent angiogram, with them saying I could die without it.

With no risk factors apart from a family history of heart disease, I and the cardiologist were bewildered at the thought of a heart attack. During the angiogram, the doctor asked if I had been under a lot of stress to which I answered yes, that my friend had just died, and they diagnosed me as having Broken Heart Syndrome.

Fortunately, the treatment was much the same as for SCAD. However, I continued to have shocking back pain which led them to a repeat angiogram three days later, where my SCAD was diagnosed. I remained in hospital for a few more days, nine in total and was discharged home. Oh my God, how scary that was! I felt OK but was pretty weak and tired very easily. It was totally impossible to stop thinking about a potentially early death sentence with an eight-year-old boy that needs me. My husband did not cope well at all and I had my sister come and stay with me for a few days.

As the weeks slowly went by, I began to feel stronger physically but mentally a mess. I did ten weeks of cardiac rehabilitation which was fantastic, apart from my meltdown on day one with all of the typical, old male heart patients in my class. I felt like I should be working there, not being a patient! By the end of my time, there were a few other women and two of them were younger than me!

I began to see a psychologist to help me with my 'adjustment disorder', as it was termed, and had ten sessions with her. This was a great help to be able to speak about my fears and frustrations completely openly and honestly without having to put on a brave face for everyone. I found the psychological side of it the hardest to deal with and also required anti-depressant medication to deal with my anxiety. I am unable to return to my old job doing night shift, but have returned to just doing two day shifts on weekends. I am pleased to say that after fourteen months, I am feeling back to normal albeit a bit tired. I am surprised that it took me so long to recuperate especially psychologically. I am now just taking Aspirin, Nebilet and Ramipril.

There is a light at the end of the tunnel, which I never thought would shine.

Lynne Clark – 25th June 2016 – Aged 49

At the time of my SCAD, at the age of 49, I was in the best physical shape I had been in for years. Most weekday mornings, I began the day with a gym class, alternating weights with spin classes. Sugar had been given up two years before and in the last 12 months, I had been fully embracing a healthy diet of no processed food. Work had been stressful for a number of years and I had been studying on top of an almost full-time job. Things were looking more positive though as I finished my study and started a new dream job in March 2016.

A few weeks prior to starting my new job, I came down with a strep infection that I thought just would not give up. After a couple of weeks of antibiotics, my blood test came back clear, but I still didn't feel quite right. I was more tired than usual and I was getting dizzy at the gym. I went back to my GP and then another GP, but it seemed like it was just taking a while to get over the virus. A test of my blood pressure between sitting and standing showed a difference of 28 points, but still no answers.

In May, we decided to book a cruise to celebrate my 50th birthday. My thoughts at the time were, *If I have to turn 50, I'm doing it laying by a pool with a book in one hand and a cocktail in the other.* How differently I think now. I was still not feeling right when exercising but was frustrated with not getting answers and decided I was just going to push through it. I remember on the Thursday before my SCAD, I increased my weights in my P9 class.

On Saturday, June 25th 2016, I woke a bit tired as I hadn't slept that well the night before but got up and we went and watched my son's soccer game. Afterwards, my husband and I went to do our normal grocery shop. In the car, I yawned, felt really tired and had an ache across my back between my shoulders. I put it down to the heavier weights two days before. It went away and we did the shopping without incident and came home. I was standing in the kitchen, putting away groceries when I just didn't feel right. I turned to talk to my husband but my knees went and there was a grey tunnel closing in. According to Steve, my knees buckled and then I just hit the floor backwards.

We are not sure how long I was unconscious. My heart had stopped and I had stopped breathing, causing a hypoxic seizure. Steve thought I was gone. Luckily, I woke up on the floor, feeling very dazed and confused. The wait for the ambulance felt like forever but was only 20 minutes. One ridiculous thing that sticks in my mind was noticing the amount of dog hair under the sofas.

The paramedics were initially unsure why I had collapsed. As a relatively young, very fit woman with no risk factors, a heart attack seemed unlikely. However, as soon as the ECG showed inverted T-waves, he popped an Aspirin under my tongue. Similarly, at the LGH, they were unsure of what had happened until my troponin came back extremely high. The cardiologist on call was debating whether to perform an angiogram that night or wait until Monday. I think I was still in denial, as I remember arguing that I had to go to work on Monday. There were very strange looks from the doctors and my husband when I said that. I still remember being asked to rate the pain and getting frustrated because I didn't have pain, just a bit of nausea.

The young cardiologist was trying to contact the senior consultant but his phone was off. In the end, he contacted another doctor and at 9pm, I was wheeled into the cath lab for an angiogram. Once again, I had been lucky that it was a distal LAD and too small to stent.

Three more days spent in the cardiac unit with three other patients, all much older and more typical cardiac cases. Due to the seizure, there were also MRI and EEG tests to do. I was discharged on the following Tuesday and still really confused as to what had happened. The senior cardiologist was not known for good patient communication skills. I left the hospital with a bag of medication, instructions not to drive until I had seen the neurologist and a medical certificate for one week.

Fortunately, I was able to see my GP later in the week and he was very supportive. He advised me that I could see another cardiologist and gave me a referral. He also provided another week off work. In hindsight, I was silly to go back to full-time work after only two weeks, but seeing as it was a new job, I was concerned I may be put off. My GP also arranged an appointment for a care plan and private cardiac rehab. My new cardiologist was very patient and for the first time talked about SCAD.

When I left the hospital, I was given Metoprolol, Tricagrelor, Aspirin and recommended a statin. I was already taking Perindopril due to kidney issues. There were a few robust conversations with my doctors over my refusal to take the statin but as I did not have a cholesterol issue, I could not see the point. I am very grateful to the SCAD support group for the link to the research, advising they are not good for us. My body did not take well to the Metoprolol and I gained around 7 kg.

One of the most difficult aspects of this time was the driving ban imposed by the neurologist. As there had been a seizure, I was unable to drive for six months. This created all sorts of issues at work, as my job was an outreach one. Although management were supportive, it did create pressure within the team. For six months, I was reliant on taxi vouchers and limited in the distance I could travel. At home, I was completely dependent upon my husband, as there is no public transport where we live. For someone who has always been fiercely independent, the psychological impact of this was very hard to cope with.

In October, I went for an Echo Cardiogram and was very happy to find out that the artery had healed. I was able to stop the blood thinners straight away. With input from my cardiologist, my GP and I came to an arrangement about the beta blockers – as long as I wear a heart rate monitor, I could trial coming off them. My Fitbit is my new best friend and I feel so much better. Now I still take the Aspirin and Perindopril and will for the rest of my life.

One of the most useful parts of my recovery has been my rehabilitation plan and seeing an exercise physiologist. He started me with very gentle exercise and has explained clearly what I can and cannot do. I am now back at the gym five mornings a week, just in a modified way. I have my own plan for core exercises, use light weights and keep my heart rate under 130bpm.

The hardest part has been the psychological adjustment. Early on, I felt a lot of 'why me?', but then again 'why not?'. I have always hated limits and, in the past, used them as a challenge to overcome. It was difficult adjusting to what I could and couldn't do. There have been a few scary moments when I have wondered if it is happening again and two more trips to the LGH. Sometimes it feels like I am walking around with a ticking time bomb inside my chest. Mostly I am grateful that I am still here with my amazing husband and two beautiful children. We did go on my 50th birthday cruise, only now it was more of a celebration that I have turned 50. Yes, there was no diving but there was some snorkelling in some stunningly beautiful reefs. There were no cocktails but a lovely glass of bubbles on the day and time to reflect on a scary eight months and on how lucky I am to be here with my family and friends.

Brenda Stubbs – 4th March 2010 – Aged 40

It has taken me a long time to sit down and write my SCAD story. Initially, I felt that my SCAD events were minor in comparison to other 'SCADsters', but that is why it is so important for us all to write our stories. Yes, our initial presentations may be widely varied, but each and every one of us now on the survivors list want to make a difference. To increase awareness of SCAD, find out the why and, personally for me, whether this has a genetic link that may impact my two daughters' lives.

My first event was 4th March 2010, I woke at midnight to an 'odd' feeling. Over the years, you have many aches and pains but for some reason, the overwhelming feeling was that this shoulder blade ache was 'not right'. Then came the feeling of nausea and cold sweats. As a nurse, I knew what the symptoms could mean, but at 40, with no family history, and being relatively fit with a normal BMI (sound familiar?), I was fighting my own diagnosis.

Living 40 minutes out of town and not wanting to be melodramatic and call an ambulance, we decided to drive to the hospital. Leaving my 12- and 10-year-old daughters at home in bed. As a shift worker, they were used to comings and goings at strange hours, and I was also thinking we may be home before they woke up (who was I kidding). As we were travelling in, the pain became more pronounced down my left arm.

One good thing with heart-related issues…no wait in the ED. Initially, I had changes on my ECG and they were thinking pericarditis. I spent the rest of the night and most of the following day in the ED until my bloods showed my troponin levels rising and the cardiac team decided to take me for an angiogram. They found an occlusion in my distal left anterior descending artery, which they tried to pass a wire through, but were unable to. Leaving my specialist to ask if the occlusion was due to a clot or an anatomical variant. I was in for observation for three nights and sent home on routine medications – Aspirin, Nexium, Metoprolol, Perindopril and Rosuvastatin.

Why did this happen? My cardiologist was keen to label it as Takotsubo Syndrome. Why else would a perfectly healthy 40-year-old have a 'heart attack'? This didn't sit well with me, as I didn't consider myself to be an overly anxious person, and my life situation at the time was not stressful. Besides, it happened while I was asleep!

A recommendation from my sestambi rest/stress study the following April was to have another follow-up rest sestambi in two months. I had to push to have this done, and the results subsequently ruled out Takotsubo. I also sought a second opinion from another cardiologist, who confirmed I had apical myocardial infarction and it was unlikely to be Takotsubo syndrome. So, I had eliminated that this event was stress related, but the closest I got to a diagnosis was my GP telling me there may have been a weakness in the wall of my artery, maybe from a viral infection as a child, and this had caused the tear which occluded my artery. It should never happen again!

I got on with my life and managed to stop all my medications over the following year. This all changed in 2015. I had been running park runs and had progressed to my first 5K fun run and yes, in life's quirky way, I was running the heart foundation's 'run for your heart.' That Sunday afternoon, I had a short episode of feeling 'odd' with nausea and cold sweats which settled after an hour or so. I ignored it, and it was not until Thursday on my morning run when I did not 'feel quite right' and had to stop and walk home. The tightness and tingling in my arms resolved but left me with a left scapula ache that did not go away, only rating as a two out of ten.

I was meant to be working that afternoon and the thought had crossed my mind to just do an ECG once I got to work.

Luckily, I came to my senses and got my husband to take me to ED (four hours after the initial signs). Probably better than having a Code called on me on my ward and giving my co-workers a 'heart attack.'

I was admitted to ED and within two hours was in the cath lab, having an angiogram and stent to my right coronary artery. Once again, I was kept for observation for three nights and discharged on routine medications – Metoprolol, Aspirin, Brilinta and Rosuvastatin.

Still no mention of SCAD by my cardiac team, BUT a big question of SCAD by my GP and myself. It was not until April 2016 when I saw my cardiologist for my six-month check that he conceded that my two cardiac events were, in fact, Spontaneous Coronary Artery Dissections.

A lot has changed in seven years, awareness and support has improved dramatically. The drive of people like Pamela and the connection provided by our Facebook group, whether you are an active user who regularly posts comments or a passive user who draws strength and comfort reading others' stories, we are joined by common ground and this is solidified by camaraderie shown at SCAD walks. Research is the way forward and we are exceptionally lucky to have the help of the Victor Chang Cardiac Research Institute.

Maree Martin – 2nd January 2016 – Aged 58

I had never heard of Spontaneous Coronary Artery Dissection and certainly didn't expect that I would ever experience a heart attack. I was 58 years old, active, not overweight, a healthy, non-smoker with normal blood pressure and cholesterol levels but life events during the previous four years had provided a considerable degree of stress. Saturday, 2nd January 2016, was quite a hot day and I was looking forward to our family gathering together for lunch later that day. In the morning, I decided to go for a 6-km walk around our local estuary, which I had done several times before over the years. I didn't take any water with me but I felt quite comfortable during the walk. When I returned to the car, it was like an oven and I remember feeling very hot and tired on the drive home and thought that I'd become a little dehydrated. The walk had taken longer than I'd expected, so once home, I quickly rushed to prepare lunch for the family. As we were finishing our meal, my husband noticed a suspicious person lurking around my son's car which was parked on our front lawn. I quickly rose from my chair to have a look for myself when I felt a sharp, stinging pain in the top of my chest on the left side, below my collarbone.

I didn't say anything to anyone but walked down the passage-way towards the bathroom, thinking I'd strained a muscle whilst on my walk. Suddenly, I began to feel a little queasy and then noticed a slight ache on the inside of my left arm. At that moment, I jokingly thought to myself, *I hope I'm not having a heart attack!*

I made my way to the family room to sit down and commented to my husband that I had a pain in my chest, to which he replied, "It's probably just indigestion!" Over the next few minutes, the pain began to ease into a dull ache, but did not go away. I felt no sense of urgency as we waved the children goodbye around 2:30pm but I asked my husband to take me to the hospital "just in case".

Upon arriving at the Emergency Dept., I was very quickly assessed by a doctor who ordered an ECG and blood tests. The tests were all normal but I had to wait for the results of a second troponin test before getting the all clear. I didn't present as a typical heart attack patient, so it was expected that I'd be going home that night. Everything changed when the results showed that I had a raised troponin level. I remember asking the nurse if that meant I'd had a heart attack and when she said yes, I panicked. Suddenly, I couldn't breath and my heart was racing out of control – I was having a panic attack.

I was given Aspirin, an injection of morphine and a wafer under my tongue and then transferred to ICU, where I stayed for two days. During that time, I felt perfectly fine, all my ECGs were completely normal and I began to wonder whether they'd misdiagnosed me.

I was transferred to the Coronary Care Unit within the hospital on the Monday and saw a cardiologist that morning. An angiogram was performed straight away and during the procedure, I remember the cardiologist saying it was SCAD and no treatment was necessary, as it would heal on its own. It had occurred in the distal posterior descending branch of my right coronary artery. The cardiologist basically explained that little is known about SCAD but it appears to affect mainly women. I was prescribed a list of medications that are standard for every heart attack patient and discharged on the Wednesday.

The following weeks were a blur of anxiety, stress and hyper-vigilance. Every twinge or slight pain caused me so much angst and concern. Although my family were very supportive, I felt extremely anxious and bewildered with my diagnosis. I googled as much as I could but everything mentioned it being rare and that there was no known cause.

Thankfully, about four months later, I happened to hear a broadcast on my local radio station in which Pam McKenzie was being interviewed. When I heard SCAD mentioned, I couldn't believe it. Here was someone else who had experienced this strange heart event and she had started a Facebook group for others who wanted to share their experiences. I can't describe how relieved I was to know that there were other people willing to reach out through this forum and in doing so have provided the support I needed to help me move forward. Through the information sharing provided by members, I've become aware of the important research work the Victor Chang Institute here in Australia and institutions such as the Mayo Clinic in America are undertaking, trying to find answers to questions about what causes SCAD.

I have been told by my cardiologist that my heart has completely healed now but it is still a difficult and ongoing process for me to regain my confidence around exercise and exertion. Anxiety is more difficult to manage but I am hopeful that over time, this will improve for me as it has for many others in this situation – one day at a time.

Danuta Teresiak – 13th April 2016 – Aged 48

My name is Danuta Teresiak.

I have always been slim, lead a healthy lifestyle, exercised and had normal cholesterol and low blood pressure.

On 13th April 2016, at the age of 48, I was with my daughter on our way to work. Whilst walking to the train station, I felt a sudden onset of pain in my left arm, starting from my jaw down to my wrist. I also felt a little bit breathless. As we walked up the ramp at the train station, the pain worsened and I felt faint.

My daughter recognised these symptoms as a heart attack and alerted the train station staff, who immediately called the ambulance.

The paramedics treated me with Aspirin and GTN. My pain went away approx. 15 mins after arriving at the hospital. The first blood tests showed that my troponin level was raised to 12 and the second to 402. I was told that I had a heart attack and that I would have to stay in hospital and have an angiogram the following day.

I couldn't believe what I was hearing, because I always thought that I was fit and healthy and a heart attack was the last thing I would expect. However, what I didn't know was that things were going to get worse.

At approx. 6pm the same day, the pain in my left arm returned, but this time, it was a lot more severe. Whilst lying on the hospital bed, I passed out and when I woke up, I saw a lot of doctors and nurses fussing over me. I was again treated with medications and rushed to the cath lab for an emergency angiogram. I was diagnosed with SCAD in a small artery on the left side under my heart. Luckily, I didn't have a stent put in. I spent the next six days in hospital because my blood pressure was very low and my heart rate very fast. I was put on Aspirin, Plavix, Metoprolol and Atorvastatin. My troponin level peaked at 45,000. I have been told that I have 10% damage to my heart.

After I was discharged from the hospital, I spent 2.5 months at home, as I felt too weak to return to work. I had bad side effects from the medications and my cardiologist decided to take me off all medications, except for Aspirin. Four months after my SCAD, I attended my daughter's wedding and I was so grateful that I was there to witness this happy moment.

I now feel much better and almost back to normal physically, but I am scarred psychologically, as every little ache in the chest area scares me and I get very anxious. I am now practising meditation and it helps to keep me calm.

It was a terrible experience to go through, but I am thankful that I'm still here and grateful to my daughter for her quick thinking in getting me the help that I needed.

Sam Allan – 18th September 2016 – Aged 33

Well, where do I start? My name is Sam Allan, I live in Bowen, North Queensland, and I was 33 years old when my heart attack/dissection happened, so quite a scary thing to go through.

I lived a pretty hectic life at times, some days were more stressful than others, especially with raising a teenage daughter on my own. I worked all week and enjoyed having drinks and catching up with mates on the weekend.

It was Saturday, 18th September 2016 (a day which will be etched in my mind for a very long time), what I thought was a normal night out for me. I was at our local yearly fishing classic at the beach, then walked up to the pub a few hours later and sat there for a few hours, talking to mates, only drinking water by this stage. Then all of a sudden, I started getting really sweaty and felt like I was going to spew, so I walked to the toilet, which didn't help. So, then I walked outside the pub to another mate and he said, "Sammy are you okay?"

By this stage, I said, "No, I don't think I am. I need to go home." So then I got dropped off at home by another mate. When I got there, I managed to walk up two flights of stairs, washed my face and then went to bed about 2am.

Around 3:30am, I woke to what was the most horrible pain/discomfort I have ever experienced in my life, like someone sitting on my chest and what felt like a really bad case of heartburn. I couldn't get comfortable sitting, standing or laying down, so thought I would go out to the kitchen and get a few heartburn tablets. As I went out, I was staggering

66

and hitting the walls like I was really, really drunk and the funny thing was, I didn't even drink much.

I went back to bed and by this time, I was spewing up bile, I was sweating like I have never sweated before. I tried jumping, punching and hitting this thing out of my chest, but nothing was working. I also read somewhere if you think you're having a heart attack to cough, which I didn't think I was having but thought anything was worth a try, so let's do it. Nope, that didn't work either, this 'thing', whatever it was, just wasn't budging.

I decided to have a cool shower because that usually makes you feel a bit better. I fell over in there, eventually got myself up, got out, then checked in my daughter's room but thought, nope, it's too complicated to wake her up. So, I continued walking to my room to get dressed and thought to myself what the heck was going on. Sweat was pouring out of me like I had a tap turned on above my head. I was in so much pain, something I never ever want to experience again. I didn't know what to do, so after four hours of trying to do what I could, I thought bugger it, I'd better get some help. I texted my mum 'HELP! Hospital, quick'. She then called me and asked, "What's going on?"

And I said, "Get here now."

She replied that I really should call an ambulance. I said, "Nah, it will be okay, you just take me up to get checked over," in a really slurry, pained voice.

I still don't know how I managed to walk down the two flights of stairs. The hospital trip is very vague, I remember getting to the back door at emergency and the nurse getting me in a wheelchair, then saying to my mum, "OMG, she doesn't look very well at all." I remember having blood tests, a troponin test and an ECG (which was all over the place) being done but don't even remember the nurses taking my clothes off to put a catheter in or much of anything else. Then I found out I was having a massive heart attack.

I got airlifted to Townsville hospital, which is two hours away from my home town. I don't remember the chopper ride, I was passed out on and off till about ten minutes out, they did tell me I had chest pain while on there though. I was taken to CCU, where I stayed for a bit. It was in there where I eventually got to see my daughter, she was so frightened, that seriously broke my heart and I just wanted to cry. Later that day, I had an angiogram done, the surgeon said, "It looks like your drink was spiked." Then they found I had a coronary artery dissection and am very, very lucky to be alive and which was also apparently very rare for my age.

So, a fun night out for me turned into an absolute nightmare. The nurses and doctors from Bowen called Townsville Hospital to ask if I made it, because they said I was pretty much at death's door and they were very concerned about me, which was lovely of them.

I had to stay in hospital for one month as I was too high risk to go anywhere. Spent lots of weeks in the cardiac ward and I'd become part of the furniture.

I celebrated my 34th birthday in there the best I could with family, friends and lots of presents. I had lots of tests and scans over the following month but it's not somewhere I want to be in a hurry again. I was initially set to have a bypass but a 2nd angiogram a month later confirmed the dissection had healed and that there were no narrowings or blockages, I had to have an echocardiogram, where they confirmed I had heart failure, so my heart is functioning at 35%. I also have microvascular angina. Then the words came out that I had been happy to hear but also dreading...that I could go home.

Umm, how could I go home? How do I live this new life? What if something happens to me? I don't have a nurse or doctor a buzz away, I'm too far away for help, what do I do? Aaahhhh, lots of thoughts running through my mind.

I will admit life has been a big struggle for the last eight months, to go from being so independent and doing everything for myself. Some days I now find it hard to go about my day with the usual housework, hanging out washing, even to do grocery shopping. I am at the doctors weekly for check-ups, as he is still very concerned about the symptoms I am getting, which are light headedness (which I think is due mostly from very low blood pressure), chest pain on and off, shortness of breath, numbness down my left arm, pain between my shoulder blades and just feeling generally unwell.

I have had about ten visits to the Emergency Department earlier in the year, where troponin tests and ECG are done each time and have come back negative or borderline. For someone who had never been in a hospital, only for one day, giving birth to my child, it seems that's where my new home was.

I returned to work on restricted hours and restricted duties three months after 'the event', but that didn't last long, as I nearly passed out and got sent home and wasn't allowed to return until I was sorted out. It has now been four months since then and I am allowed to go back next week on even more restricted hours and duties then last time. I am still getting lightheaded, etc., but I will just have to rest. Luckily for me, I work for a fantastic company who have been helping me through it all and are now helping with the return to work to make it as easy and less stressful as possible.

Unfortunately, we don't have any type of cardiac rehab here, so I have to try and do a little bit of exercise at home.

If I wake up feeling good, then I get on the exercise bike, try and do a bit of housework, go visit friends, which then makes me have to lay down for the rest of the day, because I'm buggered.

The medications I am on are Sozol, Ivabradine, Atorvastatin, Bisoprolol, Clopidogrel, Aspirin, Telimisartan, Magnesium and Nitrolingual Spray (when needed).

Although I have a wonderful support network, I still feel more alone then ever some days and I have had lots of moments where I want to scream, cry and say, "Why me? Why didn't I die when this happened? Why am I still here? Why wasn't it my time yet?" I am seeing a psychologist, exercise physiologist and a dietitian since last week, who are trying to help me with everything and it is only early days but hoping that makes a big difference.

Luckily for me, while searching Facebook one day, I found a couple of support groups about heart attacks and heart failure and this one, which gave me some relief, as there are finally people out there who know what you're going through.

I will say, yes, my life has changed dramatically, and it will never ever be the same again. But I guess you just have to do what you can and get on with life the best you can, learn to lean on your friends and family a bit more and don't be afraid to ask for help when you need it.

I am glad I am still here to tell my story and it does make me appreciate life even more now and not worry about the petty stuff, I get to watch my daughter grow up, be there for my friends and family, because honestly, without them all, I wouldn't have got through it.

So, thank you to all of those people who have stuck by me, I really do appreciate it.

Helen Campion – 17th January 2015 – Aged 47

On 17th January 2015, my daughter and I set out on our C25K (couch to five kilometre) run.

I had just finished a 12-hour shift in the ICU where I worked as a nurse. We had just finished our five-minute warm-up and it was raining and I was complaining, as usual. "I'm lazy, it's hot, I'm tired." You get the picture.

I was a fit, active 47-year-old woman, who spent a lot of time outdoors, climbing mountains, bush walking, sightseeing around the area, gardening, always busy. But on this evening, as we moved from our fast walk to a slow jog, I said to her with a laugh in my voice, "I think I'm going to have to stop, I don't feel very well." With that, I stumbled into her, she turned around, preparing to give me a good-natured scolding to spur me on, only to be faced with a mother who had turned grey.

I promptly fell to the ground, proceeded to have some type of hypoxic seizure. She hailed a passing taxi while calling 000 and together they did CPR, QAS arrived and delivered a shock and my rhythm returned to one compatible with life.

I was combative and not appropriated, so the decision to intubate me was made.

I was transported back to the hospital I had left only one short hour ago. I spent some time in the emergency department, stabilised and then taken to the intensive care unit to be cared for by the very people I worked side by side with. That is confronting to for everyone.

For three days, they kept me sedated and intubated while they worked out what had happened. A CT angiogram showed I'd had a SCAD of the LAD. They stented this, took out the tube and sent me home five days later.

I don't appear to have any brain damage, although because of my medical back ground, I feel as though there I do, but my family assure me I am still just as I was before the SCAD. Despite the fact I like to claim a 'hypoxic brain injury' every time I do something outrageously stupid, they won't let me get away with this.

I'm angry it happened to me. I don't drink, nor do I smoke, I exercised every day. I do, and have done, all the right things, and still this terrible thing happened to me.

I went back to work a few months later. I struggle to understand why this happened to me. Like everyone else, I will never know the answers to these questions but I am grateful that I am still here and that to the outside world, I still look the same, no obvious brain damage, thank you generous, courageous competent CPR bystander, my daughter Rebecca and the selfless, tireless QAS officers, Luke, Struan and the others who are nameless but no less important.

All the stars aligned for me that evening and I am grateful.

Karen Herrmann – August 2015 – Aged 47

My name is Karen Herrmann. I live in the Sutherland Shire in Sydney. Ever since high school, I've been an average height, slim, 50kg competitive athlete, except during my four pregnancies. In August 2015, when I was 47 years old, on a Friday afternoon whilst energetically cleaning the outdoor spa, I began to feel pain in my chest. It gradually worsened over half an hour until left arm pain also began. I suddenly felt hot and nauseous. My first reaction was to head to the phone to call someone (or an ambulance) for help.

However, when I picked up the handset, it was dead, as there was an extremely rare Shire-wide electricity blackout most of that day. My mobile only had 2% charge, so I sent a text to my eldest daughter, Amy, a physiotherapist, asking her what my symptoms might be. I knew they were heart attack or stroke symptoms but was in denial that could happen to a young, fit person. I was hoping she would tell me I'd just strained something and to take it easy. Unfortunately, she didn't receive my message until two hours later when she finished her shift and I'd been deliriously resting on the lounge. She headed straight to me whilst, in the meantime, my 2nd eldest daughter, Bree, arrived home and sat close by, as she knew it wasn't normal for me to nap on the lounge.

Amy suggested immediately it was a heart attack and prepared to take me to hospital. I was still in denial as she pointed out that elite athletes drop dead of heart attacks. Strangely, once I stood up from the lounge, the pain all disappeared and I felt fine. Amy was heading away for the weekend, so I told her to go and promised that if my pain returned, I would call the doctor.

Later that evening, the chest and left arm pain returned whilst I was hanging washing on the clothes airer inside. My husband was now home and insisted on taking me straight to hospital as he was concerned I hadn't gone earlier when it first happened.

The ED staff and cardiologist at Sutherland Hospital were fantastic and very efficient. I was given an angiogram as soon as possible and SCAD was diagnosed. A stent was not inserted, as the cardiologist was concerned that due to the tear being at the distal end of the LAD artery, the upper end of the artery could be damaged during such a procedure. Instead, I had total bedrest in hospital for five days and further rest at home for a few weeks to enable the artery to heal. The cardiologist hoped at the time that six months later, it would look like I'd never had a heart attack. Unfortunately, that wasn't the case. I have sustained damage to the heart and probably have to stay on blood thinners and other medications long term.

So, within a few months, I went from being a medication-free Australian Masters Athletics 800m champion to a medication-dependant heart attack survivor. I still train with my 12-year-old daughter, Cloe, as I've always coached her, but I can no longer compete myself. It's a small price to pay for being able to be here and watch my four beautiful children grow up. I recently had the wonderful experience of being 'mother of the bride' to Amy and this year seeing Bree complete university, my son Jarrod start and Cloe start high school.

The whole experience certainly taught me a lot about a condition I never knew existed and I try to inform as many as I can to be aware. In the meantime, I appreciate life more and try to spend more time relaxing, as I used to be a bit too busy. It's taught me that life certainly is precious.

Marissa Simmons – 26th April 2014 – Aged 43

The 26th of April 2014 is one day I will never forget. It started as quite a cruisy Saturday, just hanging about the house with my two daughters playing, reading and a bit of spring cleaning, I was feeling very chilled and content. My husband suggested that afternoon we should go to our friend's restaurant for an early dinner with the girls.

I began to get the girls ready and then moved on to myself, while I was getting ready, I had a very sharp pain in my head with an overwhelming feeling that came over my body, I thought maybe I was being struck down with some sort of virus; however, things started happening quite quickly from there, one after the other, my heart felt like it was getting hand washed and my left arm started feeling very heavy like my whole body weight had shifted over to just that arm, making me feel off balance, I was holding it up because I felt like it would drag on the floor.

I came down to see my husband to let him know what I was going through and suggested he drive me to the hospital instead of dinner. He immediately started googling signs of a heart attack as his friend had one two weeks prior. He said, "Oh my god, it sounds like the same sort of symptoms." As this was happening, the pain in my jaw was unbearable. I didn't want him to call an ambulance (silly move) as I didn't want to frighten my then two- and six-year-old daughters, so we drove instead, I could feel the pain intensifying. As we approached emergency, I jumped out of the car and ran in while he parked the car with the girls.

I said to the receptionist, "Please, could you help me? I think I'm having a heart attack."

It's like she didn't believe me, she sort of rolled her eyes and said, "C'mon through," still not taking me seriously. I was dressed up on my way out, so this may have thrown the hospital staff (always best to call an ambulance).

When through, an elderly man came over with the stretcher with no urgency whatsoever, I was frightened and worried and really felt no one gave a damn. The doctors on duty asked me a variety of questions and it was not until the ECG report came back, which I might add didn't take long at all, that action began to happen. They were then moving very quickly, there were doctors all around me, phone calls being made, as the doctor who performs the stent procedure was not present but on call, this was all happening in front of my daughters and I looked over at my husband and said, "The girls have seen enough, please take them home." My family left with some reservation; however, it was for the best. My husband didn't know when he returned if I would still be here or not, but we had to do what was best for the girls.

The doctor arrived as I was being prepared for theatre. I went up for surgery and discovered later that I had two stents to my LAD artery and spent the next six nights in hospital. I slowly came off my meds, except for Ramipril and Aspirin daily.

My blood pressure played up once I gave birth to my first daughter and at 34 weeks pregnant with my second daughter, I strongly believe this irregularity with my blood pressure had something to do with it, as my high/irregular blood pressure continued once I gave birth and would rise when I had my period. I also started intense training more than what I was used to, I have always exercised, but this was on another level.

Three years on and I still live with the fear of it happening again; however, my children keep me busy, happy and sort of positive. I try to conquer a lot of my fears, like travelling away from hospitals, camping and visiting foreign places, as I know my children need to experience life and I would hate it if I was stopping them from doing that. Even though life is very different now, the show must go on for my sake and my family...

Ricci Smith – 27th September 2011 – Aged 55

It was the 27th of September 2011 and my sister's birthday. I was 55 years old, with no health issues such as high blood pressure, cholesterol, etc., and reasonably fit but overweight.

I had my two eldest grandchildren at home with me, as they were on their school holidays. About 11am, I got a phone call from my youngest son, who lived around the corner, asking if I could pick him up and could he use my car, as his wouldn't start. I did this, he dropped me off back at home and I was checking my emails when I got a radiating pain to the left of my chest. I then got a similar pain in the inside of my left elbow.

I had recently seen on the TV show *The Drs* that if you ever had these symptoms to take Aspirin, so I took 5 x 30mg tablets.

By now, I was feeling nauseous and called my husband, who was working out of the district that day. I told him I was going to call an ambulance but I would talk to the nurse on call first, which I did, as I had received a fridge magnet in the post a few months previous. The nurse began to ask questions like what symptoms were presenting.

By now, I had cold sweats and light headiness. She then instructed me to sit down and said she had an ambulance on its way. As quickly as it started, all my symptoms had now subsided. A paramedic on his own arrived soon after and began hooking me up to a portable ECG machine and blood pressure taken. For the first time in my life, it was high, and he also said there were a few squiggly lines on my ECG that shouldn't be there.

An ambulance with two more paramedics arrived and the questions started, like was I on any medications, but 'no' was my answer to that and every other question about me having high blood pressure, cholesterol, diabetes or illnesses, etc. The only thing was the weight which had creeped up over the past five or six years. I was given two GTN tablets under my tongue and conveyed to our local A and E Dept. at Latrobe Regional Hospital. The questioning began again but as I had no symptoms, the doctors thought I had angina. Bloods were taken to be sent to the lab and the usual tests, ECG, etc., were done. In no time, the blood test came back that the troponin acid levels were up, which really surprised the treating doctor, as he said I wasn't really the usual heart attack patient and I would be tested again after three hours, which, when done, also showed the levels had risen again. It was then decided I would be admitted into the Critical Care Unit overnight to be reassessed the next morning.

After a sleepless night, it was decided I would have breakfast and go home and an appointment would be made to travel to Melbourne and have an angiogram within the next two weeks. Someone looking over me decided this was going to happen much sooner and whist having breakfast, my symptoms started up again just as they had the previous day. With that, the doctors made plans to convey me ASAP by ambulance to Monash Heart, Clayton Hospital in Melbourne, which is one and half hours from home. I arrived there that night to a wonderful, caring staff and the next morning, I was given the angiogram.

A few hours or so after the angiogram, a doctor came to see me, drew a diagram and explained I had had a Spontaneous Cardiac Artery Dissection in the LAD but said it could not be stented, as it was in the distal part of the artery, which is the narrow part leading into the heart. He also said they would treat me conservatively with the usual six medications given to heart attack patients. I couldn't believe how calm I was with all that was happening to me and took it all in my stride. I still remember how sick I felt taking these medications, so I was also given anti-nausea tablets as well. A day after the angiogram, I was put in a ward with three other heart patients, all males, and we soon found ourselves having a few laughs over one of the gents who smoked like a train and couldn't wait to get out to have a beer. The next day, I was released.

That's when my reality began and I felt scared and insecure not being in a hospital. For the next few weeks, I had several appointments with doctors, a heart scan done and a few other tests, etc., which all came back that things were progressing well. I went in depression and anxiety, went back to my GP, who sent me to have free counselling with a psychologist under the Medicare Mental Health Care plans, which gave me ten free visits.

Every time I had a slight pain in my chest caused through heartburn or a muscle, I would panic, and twice got my husband to call an ambulance. The A and E staff were very good to me and although my ECG, blood pressure and bloods were good, I'd be panicking. The staff would put me at ease and tell me to come back if ever I felt worried at all.

I was taken off most of the medication over a short time, as I didn't tolerate them well, except for Atenolol and Aspirin. They were the only two medications I remained on. About two years ago, I found a white lace-patterned rash in my mouth, which a skin specialist diagnosed as Lichen Planus, which is a result of the Atenolol, so that was also dropped. I only take Aspirin now, which I have chosen to do.

Although it has been coming up to six years now since my SCAD event, I still have moments where I think why me and then I think why not me, I have experienced something that is quite rare and I have learnt so much about myself and others. I do believe everything happens for a reason. I have light moments where I think if I was to have something which occurs one in so many million, why couldn't have been something like my numbers coming up in Tatts Lotto. LOL…

Hoping our stories will bring some awareness to this very rare heart event which mainly affects females. Many thanks to Pamela McKenzie for starting this group that brings together people from all over Australia who have experienced this occurrence.

Dominique Chevrant-Breton – 30th December 2016 – Aged 53

Hi there!

My name is Dominique. I am a 53-year-old slim, fit, active woman; my diet is really good (I'd like to think so) and I exercise every day at my local friendly gym. I have a full-time job and a 22-year-old son living at home with me. Work can be a bit stressful and I am trying to manage this as best as possible.

30th December 2016 was a hot day in Sydney and I was enjoying the Christmas to New Year short holiday. That morning, I had gone to the gym as usual, did a strength/circuit class, had coffee with a gym buddy and was then at home, reading a book on the lounge under the ceiling fan. Late afternoon, I started having some bad chest pain – as if an elephant was sitting on my chest!!! The pain continued throughout the night, radiating to my right shoulder. I thought, *Surely, this is not a heart attack, not me, I have none of the risk factors and no heart disease in my family. I must have pulled some muscle at the gym.* I felt better the next morning and did a spin class, sweating more than usual, but again, the heat was relentless. I took myself to the medical centre after the gym and the GP ordered some blood tests.

By then, it was New Year's Eve. 6pm, I was watching the news on TV when the pathology laboratory called me and told me to call an ambulance immediately and go to the hospital: my blood tests showed evidence of significant heart damage (my troponin levels were about 800!). Ambulance on New Year's Eve, cardiac ward for a few days, with a battery of

80

tests, including ECG, ultrasound, and finally an angiogram, which revealed a SCAD. I was discharged on 2nd January with the standard cocktail of drugs (Aspirin, blood thinners, beta blockers and statin!!!). Everyone close to me – myself included – were baffled by the news. But I am known to like a challenge and I thought that whatever it takes, I'll do it and get better!

Today is Australia Day – so not even four weeks after my SCAD – and I am pleased to advise that the cardiologist has now asked me to stop all the medications and to remain on Aspirin only. I am very relieved, as the side effects were not pleasant. I am back at the gym, with gradual progression of efforts.

My life is back to normal, although I am a bit more moderate in my efforts for the time being. I know there is a chance of recurrence, but if it does happen, I know all the signs and will go to the hospital immediately. Any chest pain lasting more than ten minutes, call 000. I guess my SCAD was relatively minor compared to others, and I feel blessed.

If you are on Facebook, look up SCAD, there are a few groups out there, including an Australian one, and you will feel less alone! Take care and one step at a time!

Melanie Louden – 28th May 2015 – Aged 43

It was Wednesday morning. I was rushing my raisin toast whilst preparing the kids' school lunches before I'd head off for work. I thought to myself, *I really need to slow down and chew my food properly,* as I could feel indigestion developing. I turned my head to ask the person who was sitting on my left arm to please "get off"! I had felt this sensation a few days earlier and was pleased I was able to will it away, blaming a busy weekend. It woke me from my sleep. I ignored that too.

We had had a great overseas trip to New Zealand over Christmas. Then the year went downhill from there. My husband had a surfing accident, rupturing his kidney. He spent a month in hospital. The hospital was an hour from home, in Newcastle.

During that time, my eldest child started a new school and in the first few days, a child in her class tragically lost his life in a boating accident. I was working almost full time in two jobs and studying when the kids went to bed. I was 43 years of age. Healthy. Could have been fitter but not overweight. I was diagnosed with idiopathic hypertension at age 40 and was managing that with medication. There is atherosclerosis and heart disease in my family. Registered nurse. Married to my first year of university sweetheart, with three beautiful children, aged 7, 9 and 11, at that time.

I went into the bedroom and checked my blood pressure. Too high! I asked my husband could he take the kids to school so I could drive myself to the local Community Hospital, as I didn't feel right. On arrival, I had an ECG, which was normal, and blood collected that was negative for troponin. Although it was too early to show up. The lovely nurses gave me a 'pink lady'. I was quite concerned about where the pink lady was going to go! It turned out to be an antacid with Lignocaine. You won't see that one on any cocktail menu!

My husband arrived and I told him that everything was normal and that I would have to stay for six hours. Hospital policy, so we decided he might as well go to work. He phoned my work to explain why I hadn't arrived and left, promising to come back at lunch time.

After an hour or so of chatting to the nurses, I knew it was time for another ECG and more bloods. I read the nurse's face and knew straight away that something wasn't right. I never experienced any pain but there was still someone sitting on my arm. My blood came back positive for troponin.

The cardiologist at John Hunter Hospital was phoned and an ambulance was sent immediately to collect me. I was given morphine and told to relax and not to move. I was transferred to the ambulance. I flicked my husband a quick text, telling him I was having a heart attack and was going to Newcastle. Not once considering the impact that might have. I lay in the back of the ambulance whilst one of my two female paramedics argued with the Community Hospital doctor over whether or not to draw up morphine for the trip. I heard the doctor raising his voice, "Time is muscle." I learnt that it was the other paramedic's first day back on the job after some time off. She looked nervous. I was feeling a little drunk. We sped off to the hospital. The driver kept apologising for the bumpy ride and then mentioned that we would be picking up Vanessa. I asked the nervous paramedic who Vanessa was. She laughed. "That morphine has kicked in!"

I heard sirens and thought that they sounded like an ambulance, then it occurred to me that it was my ambulance. I was really impressed with the care I received at the Community Hospital and was blown away with my care in ED at John Hunter. I hopped off the ambulance trolley and into a bed. I heard a doctor say, "False alarm, there is no way she is having a heart attack." The resuscitation nurse thought otherwise. Within ten minutes, I had had an ECG, cardiac echo, chest x-ray and bloods taken.

When the dust settled, the doctor looked at me puzzled. "You don't look like you are having a heart attack but your bloods and ECG are abnormal. We will admit you to the cardiac ward." I felt like a fraud.

My husband had arrived and was chatting to a doctor who had cared for him a few months earlier. On the ward, I had to wear an ECG monitor around my neck. More blood was collected. I still had no pain but I couldn't bring myself to eat anything. The cardiologist entered my space in the four-bedded room with his registrar in tow, addressing my worried husband. "Cancel the dancing girls and the keg, your wife is coming home! She has indigestion."

"She does not have indigestion," my unimpressed husband replied. I knew of him. Good cardiologist, questionable bedside manner. After putting his hand around my left breast, 'to feel my heart', I asked him had he seen my last troponin levels. He stated that he had not and went to the nurse's station to look them up. He returned quickly, stating that I was having a heart attack and was going for an angiogram immediately.

That is the moment I panicked. I knew I was allergic to contrast iodine that would have to be used in the angiogram. I feared an anaphylactic reaction. I was given antihistamines and wheeled off to theatre. To date, still one of the scariest moments of my life, I handed my jewellery over to my husband and said goodbye. I desperately wanted to see him again. I couldn't let myself think about the kids. The angiography team were amazing. I was given Fentanyl and Phenergan and drifted in and out of sleep during the procedure. Waking briefly to try and focus on the screen.

I came to in the coronary care unit, unaware of how much time had passed. I had to lie flat for six hours with a clamp on my groin. Peeing in a pan was fun! I did see my husband again though!

The next morning, I was visited by the Cardiac Rehab nurse, who was lovely but explained to me repeatedly that I'd had a heart attack. It wasn't until I burst into tears that she seemed satisfied that I understood. Thanks to my iodine allergy, my head resembled a large itchy tomato. My cardiologist turned up to see my tomato face crying. "You look terrible. I will come back later."

"No!" I demanded he stay and give me some information.

I assumed that I had inherited my family's heart disease but he told me I had no plaques in my arteries and explained that I had a tear in my left anterior descending artery and the tip was totally blocked. He insulted my intelligence by showing me a tear in his shirt so that I would understand. He said it may have been caused by a tear, plaque or embolism. He stated that there was nothing else he could do for me and that I could go home. My husband and a couple of my good friends arrived in time to keep me company whilst I waited for a big bag of medications. I was given a couple of books about heart attack with pictures of old people on the front and told to see my GP and present for cardiac rehab in a few weeks.

My world had been rocked! Seeing my children, I felt as though I had let them down. How could I have allowed them to be so reliant on me? I hadn't taught them to cook for themselves or use the washing machine. I would have to get on to that straight away. I think those thoughts protected me from the pain of considering the possibility of not seeing those little faces again.

The first week, I was very weak but recovered well after that. Slowly easing into walking down to my letterbox. My wonderful husband had Netflix connected. I was local gossip for a few days.

I returned to work. Life went on smoothly for a couple of months and then it all hit me. I would cry for no reason frequently during the day. My children would tell me about events at school and I would think, *I hope I live to see that.* After a couple of weeks, my husband suggested counselling. I agreed and approached my GP. He said, "Give it a couple more weeks and you will be fine." It wasn't the answer I was after, but he was right, and I have been fine since.

I had a bubble test to rule out a clot. It was negative.

My new cardiologist, the one who performed my angiogram, doesn't want to see me for two years. I have ceased some of my medications.

I know I got off lightly and am grateful for every day. However, the fear of it happening again haunts my thoughts sometimes when I am alone. Two years on, I still cry at times. I know I should 'get over it'. I am, it takes time.

Vanessa Duivenvoorde – 6th April 2017 – Aged 37

I am a very active person, used to running up to 20kms weekly and even completing two half marathons in the months leading up to the event that has certainly made me think about life.

On 6th April 2017, I was having lunch with a friend when I suddenly started feeling faint. It wouldn't have been the first time that I fainted, so I went to the bathroom, splashed my face, sat on the floor for a few minutes and headed back to the table. By now, my arms were starting to feel numb and I still wasn't feeling any better, so I headed home to sleep it off. After an hour or so, I was experiencing pressing pain in my chest and a stabbing pain between my shoulder blades, as well as the continuing heaviness in my arms. I phoned my ex-husband, thinking that maybe I was having a panic attack. A befriended doctor told me to lie down with my feet up and concentrate on breathing. By the time my ex arrived, the pain still hadn't got any better and the idea of having to get through the night with this kind of pain made me go to the Urgent Care Clinic to get some pain relief. My ex went to get the children from school and I walked to the clinic around the corner.

As I had indicated that 'chest pain' was the reason for my visit, I was given an ECG directly upon arrival. And from there on, things went fast! Next thing I knew, the doctor told me he had called for an ambulance because my ECG indicated that I was having a heart attack.

Hang on. I am 37 years old, don't drink, smoke or do drugs, exercise daily, have no family history of cardiovascular disease, have a healthy BMI, and I am having a what? First response to a 911 call (we live in the USA) is the fire department, so within minutes, six firemen enter the treatment room to take over my care. Another five minutes later, the ambulance arrived and they took over from the fireman. By now, my ex and children arrive too, only to see me strapped to a gurney, with a street full of fire trucks and the ambulance.

The hospital

In the ambulance, monitoring continued and two IV drips were administered. My blood pressure dropped to a dangerous level by the time we arrived at the ER. By now, it's about 5pm. The ER doctor proceeds to take blood test to test the troponin levels, and the first blood test shows increased levels, which indeed indicates that I was having a heart attack. A bed is prepared on the ICU and I am transferred there around 10pm. At midnight, another blood test is taken, and when this again shows elevated troponin levels, an angiogram is arranged for 9am the next morning. By now, the pain has subsided due to medication, and I am really not understanding how this can be happening. All night, nurses show up, running tests, checking monitors and asking me what I am doing here, young, fit and seemingly healthy. "You tell me" becomes my standard answer.

After a long, sleepless night, the morning arrives, and with that comes the angiogram. As I am wheeled into the cath lab, all I can think to myself is: *Those bloody Americans (I live in the States), always overcatering for everything, with their bloody liability stuff.* So, I got prepared for the angiogram, asked for a lot of settling drugs, and a little more, and I'm high as a kite by the time the doctor comes to do his thing. To be honest, the angiogram was painless. Didn't feel anything besides the local anaesthetic to numb my groin. After half an hour, the doctor has seen enough, and the news was that indeed they found the reason that I had a heart attack: a SCAD. This moment is where my life got turned upside down. The next news was that he was going to try and put some stents in, and if this fails, a bypass graft. So really, I went from half-marathon-running chick to possibly one with open-heart surgery in a matter of hours. Thankfully, he got the stents in place, and I was spared the open-heart surgery.

The next few hours, I felt a sense of euphoria, like a runner's high, like I cheated death. I finally managed to give my parents a call (they are in the Netherlands), "Hi, Mum, do not worry, but I just had two stents placed in my heart because I had a heart attack, but know I am on top of the world, woohoo!" After the angiogram, I was required to lay flat for about six hours and then slightly upright for another two. Writing this, and revisiting this experience, is just so unrealistic, like it was a dream.

I don't think I even realised how serious my situation was until I started getting the reactions from other people. Seeing their faces react to me having a heart attack made it hit home a bit more. From doctor friends, "Oh, the proximal LAD, that is referred to as the widow maker." (Nice!) Running buddies, "But you are the fittest person we know." (Yes indeed!) To my parents, "We are on the next flight." (Thank God for that!)

Going home

The day after the angiogram, I was ready to go home. My husband and I are separated and he took the kids for the weekend. A friend came to stay until my mother arrived. I just wasn't ready to be home alone so quickly, and it did take me a few weeks to get to that point. The first few weeks, I spend a lot of time resting. The doctor had told me that I should be fine and back on full duties, but it just wasn't happening.

My mother made sure I got the rest I needed, and I really needed it, a lot. I'd be fine out and about, and then all of a sudden, fatigue would hit, and my body just really needed to rest. My three kids were on school holidays that first week, and my ex had to go to a rig, there is no way I could have handled the kids by myself.

I think the recovery is a combination of actually recovering from the heart attack and adjusting to the medications. Looking back, my heart was already suffering for at least a week before the actual attack. I had a funny taste in my mouth, felt like I was getting a flu (like a real flu, not just a cold), didn't have my usual levels of energy. And I am so thankful that the actual event happened when it did. Two days later, I would have been halfway through a running race, and I'm afraid that the outcome wouldn't be so favourable. I am lucky that I don't require a lot of medication. I was discharged with two blood thinners (I am allergic to Aspirin) and a statin. However, I had never been on anything before, except birth control, and I feel that my body is adjusting to all this. Especially the statin, which is frustrating, because my cholesterol wasn't high to begin with. I have had numerous conversations to try and get my doctor to take me off them, but so far, no luck. Maybe when I hit the one-year mark, I'll try it again.

Five months on

Like most typical SCAD patients, I am not the 'sit-back-and-chill' type. It has limited me in doing things, like running and going out as much as I used to, but it has also added things to my life: it motivated me to complete my Masters in Public Health degree, I have even flown to Perth (from New Orleans, this is 33 hours each way) to attend the ceremony, I've been to the Netherlands for a wedding and Mexico for a vacation with the children. All these things can be done, I just need to be a lot more conscious. If I want to go out and it looks like it's a late one, I will plan a nap during the day. If I go for a run, I make sure I have enough time to rest afterwards. This is all slowly improving though. One of the things that I need to mention is the on-again, off-again chest pains that seem to linger around. At first, this worried me. I mean, I just had a heart attack! But as time passed, they seem to happen less often, and they are usually a sign that I am doing too much.

I have had a couple of follow-up appointments with my cardiologist. I don't think we are the best match. He's a bit old-school, and I do my research. However, when necessary, I did manage to pin him down and have a good Q and A with him. With this condition, that is only recently getting the light of the day, it is so important that you are your own advocate. Seek information, join SCAD survivor groups, find friends who have had the same/similar. Talk, talk, talk. If possible, look up journal articles, search the web and question your doctor. Educate others!

For me, I'll be moving back to Australia with my family in a couple of months' time (yes, ex and all). I am planning to try and do a PhD looking into recovery and rehabilitation of SCAD patients. Maybe it was the missing link that I needed to find the path I need to follow in this life. I want to use this experience and my skills as an occupational therapist and a researcher to help us.

For you who is reading this: Breath in and out, and let it all happen. Go with the flow till your body is ready to pick it all up again. If I can do it, so can you!

Kristy Do Canto – 19th June 2017 – Aged 33

At the time of my SCAD, I was a healthy 33-year-old, looking forward to embarking on a new journey, personally and professionally. I had just started a new job, a few months prior, as a deputy principal of a school close to home and due to get married to the love of my life, on 24th June 2017.

Monday, 19th June 2017, while I was driving to work, I experienced some discomfort in my chest. As there are no genetic links to heart conditions, I assumed it was anxiety in the lead up to my wedding. My wedding was planned for later in the week. I continued to drive to work and sit through a few meetings before realising the pain is not going away and that I should get it checked by the doctor.

As I couldn't get an appointment with my GP, I settled for the medical centre, having an ECG and blood test immediately, by this time, it was approximately midday. The ECG appeared clear, so I drove home, still on the understanding that I was a little stressed or anxious and that the pain was not severe enough to go to the hospital. At 6pm, I received a phone call from a different doctor from the medical centre, who told me my blood pressure and cholesterol were low, but my troponin level was high and that I should go to a hospital straight away. I had NEVER heard of the word troponin and had absolutely no idea what it even meant.

I arrived at the hospital and I was admitted straight away. By this time, the pain, which felt like pressure and not sharp pains, had increased and my troponin level had risen even further. I was having constant tests and put onto morphine. Then, all of a sudden, I heard a call over the PA in the hospital, "All available nurses to bed 3…" I looked up and realised I was in bed 3! Nurses and doctors came rushing over and defibrillator pads were stuck to my body.

At this point, all I can remember was thinking 'my time was up, I am about to die and I had not said goodbye to my loved ones'. I tried to look over to my mother and fiancé and couldn't as I was being rushed away to another room. After that, I don't remember much. The next memory I had was waking up, a doctor leaning over my bed and saying, "You have had a heart attack from an artery dissection, but you are okay and we are taking you to another room." I was wheeled into a room where my mother and fiancé were waiting. I was still a bit hazy from the anaesthetic and other medications. I looked down and saw my arm had a clear plastic band around it and was extremely tight, and I had tubes coming from my nose and three tubes from my arm. The nurses came in not long after and looked at the band on my wrist, telling me that it is very tight and they will start releasing air gradually, but it will bruise. After what I had been through, I wasn't fazed by the bruise. By this time, it was midnight and I drifted off to sleep. The nurses also explained what a SCAD heart attack was, as the term was unfamiliar to me.

The next few days consisted of tears, conversations with the cardiologist and nurses, tests and more tests. By Wednesday, the cardiologist made it clear that I would not be getting married on Saturday or going to my honeymoon in the Greek Islands the following Tuesday. Devastated, to say the least! My heart broke and disappointment crept in. My fiancé made a list of all our suppliers for the wedding and planned to cancel them all the following day (Thursday). Thursday morning arrived and my cardiologist came in early morning. He then said, "Our aim is to get you to your wedding." Music to my ears!!! I knew it was not going to be easy, coming out of hospital on the eve before my wedding day. I was fatigued and had black and blue bruises up my arms but determined to get married! I was discharged Friday night, (with a lot of medications to take) went straight to bed and woke up Saturday morning, prepared for my big day.

Despite the way I felt, the day was the best day of my life. Everything went according to plan. Follow-up appointment with my cardiologist, who then gave me the choice to go or not to go on my honeymoon. He said he would clear me to fly, though recommended it may be a good idea to wait a few months. By Monday, I felt well enough to go on my honeymoon and jet-setted off to Greece for five weeks. I had a relaxing holiday with doctors' orders to "just relax"! I am now awaiting my next follow-up appointment but feel great. I went back to work a few days after my honeymoon. I am still on the myriad of medications, which have slight side effects. I get short sharp pains in various areas of my body but none in my heart! I still feel a bit on edge and sometimes when the pain lasts longer than a few seconds, panic sets in and I think I am having another heart attack.

As a SCAD survivor, I am strong and oozing with positivity and gratitude that I am still alive to spread the message. I urge all other survivors to do the same and to stick together to find the cause and cure. Knowledge is power, and with power, we can hopefully make a difference.

Judy Maughan

I had just picked up my daughter from basketball practice and gone home and sat down with the family to eat soup. After a few mouthfuls, I suddenly felt very unwell, I decided to lie down in bed for a few minutes. Whilst resting, I began to feel pressure on my chest and an aching travelling down my right arm.

Could I be having a heart attack? My husband walked in to see how I was going. I told him I thought it best I go to hospital. Stupidly, I walked to the car!!! By the time we got there (five minutes away), I knew not to walk into emergency, I felt nauseous and a great weakness.

The ECG indicated a heart attack and the bloods confirmed the case. Straight onto an RFDS plane (thanks morphine, as it was a pretty stormy night) and into Royal Perth, they were great, thank goodness for our health system!!! We are very fortunate!

Fifteen years earlier, one month after the birth of our son, I'd had a stroke. So, in a way, I was not completely shocked by the whole event. With hindsight, and confirmation from my doctor, the stroke and SCAD heart attack are related. I have genetically high BP and although controlled, my arteries are prone to dissection. I was going through menopause at the time of the SCAD and had been very unnaturally anxious that day.

After the SCAD, the fear of reoccurrence and leaving behind my children resulted in depression. After sessions with a good psychologist and getting fit again, I have overcome the depression and been able to get on with my life! Life is great,

I have a wonderful family and a bright future. No one knows the future, but I'm sure going to try and make the most of the time I have available! Since then, I have recommenced classical ballet (last class had been when I was 14) and continued studying Italian (and visited Italy last October). SCAD is just another part of the journey, I feel gratitude for much now, the birds in the sky, the flowers and the trees and the healing powers of just being in the natural environment.

Josie Mcinerney – 8th June 2014 – Aged 51

8th June 2014 started as a normal day like every other day. My husband and I operate a small 11-room motel in an extremely busy tourist destination in regional Victoria. It was the long weekend holiday in June and Sunday is the day that we open Reception an hour later.

I've been a netball player all my life and still play in a local competition and have been an active jogger since meeting my husband over 35 years ago and jogged at least four times a week usually before work. I enjoyed participating in regular annual fun runs such as the Run4Kids, Sydney City2Surf and also would run the occasional half marathon. So, going for a 6-km jog early morning before work on Sunday was a normal routine. This particular weekend, my husband had the weekend off and was away a couple of hours from home.

About one kilometre into my run, I had a sudden sharp pain in the lower part of my sternum. It took my breath away and was quite painful. It was severe enough for me to stop running and try to breathe through the pain. When I stopped jogging, I then had a sudden wave of nausea. At this stage, I thought I may be coming down with some sort of virus and thought it best not to continue with my jog. The pain persisted, so I decided to walk back home. The pain and nausea subsided after a few minutes, so I jogged back home. I continued with my usual morning routine and headed to the motel to open Reception and start work.

About half an hour after starting work, I was stripping rooms and while picking up a basket of linen, the pain

97

sensation came back, not as severe but it persisted. Although I was able to continue working, I didn't feel quite right. Slight pain in my chest lingered and I felt a little washed out. One of my staff members convinced me to call our local hospital to get advice. The nurse I spoke to said to come in to get checked out but also said not to drive, because I had mentioned I had experienced chest pain. As I thought they were being overcautious, I drove myself to Timboon hospital (18kms).

At Timboon hospital, I had my vitals checked – pulse, blood pressure and had an ECG. All were normal. The nurse took blood and used a troponin monitor. The monitor detected troponin in my blood system but it doesn't indicate the level. The doctor was called in and more blood was taken to be sent off to the labs at Warrnambool Hospital. I had to stay put until the results came back. I wasn't feeling any pain by this stage and felt it was such an inconvenience.

After a couple of hours of sitting in a ward room, a nurse collected me and ushered me quickly back into Emergency. I was hooked up to an ECG again and other monitors and told that an ambulance was being organised to transport me to Geelong Hospital (two hours away). I was given a handful of tablets, which I was told were blood thinners, and also given injections in the stomach, which were more blood thinning medication. A quick call to my husband (and motel staff) to change plans was about the only time I had before I was in the back of the ambulance. The ambulance ride felt so surreal. Here I was sitting up with all these monitors hooked up to me, constantly being monitored and being asked did I have any chest pain when at this stage, I was feeling back to normal. I couldn't understand all the urgency and having to be transported by the only ambulance from our area. I was more concerned that the ambulance would be needed for an emergency and it was tied up transporting me!!!

More blood tests and more monitoring when I arrived at Geelong Hospital Emergency and by this stage, my husband and two sons were there too. The emergency doctor was a little surprised when he came to examine me, as I presented so healthy and well by this stage. He was a little sceptical that

I was actually the patient who had come from Timboon. Lots of questions were asked about my lifestyle, diet, family history, etc. Finally, after about an hour, the Emergency doctor sat down and gave me the news. All my bloods we good, low cholesterol, good red blood count, etc., but my troponin levels had risen further and that I'd had a suspected heart attack. Nothing prepares you for this. How can an active, healthy 51-year-old have had a heart attack? It just didn't make sense.

I was admitted to the cardiac ward at Geelong Hospital and was booked in to have an angiogram. Unfortunately, because it was the long weekend, I wasn't able to have the angiogram until the Tuesday. That full day staying in a hospital ward, constantly being monitored was the most frightening day I have ever experienced. Because at this stage, no one could tell me any more than I was been told in Emergency, I was questioning if it was going to be my last day on earth. Sounds overdramatic now, but at the time, it was so hard not to let the uncertainty overwhelm me. My family stayed with me all day and kept me occupied but the night was the most frightening, as I was so sure that if I shut my eyes, I may not wake up. It didn't help that when I was finally dozing, the nursing staff came rushing in to check on me, as they said the heart monitor alarm went off because my heart rate dropped to 39bpm. It was finally put down to my fitness and the medication that I was given over the past 24 hours.

On the day of the angiogram, I was in a bit of a daze and just went with the flow. I think it was my way of dealing with the unknown at that stage. Despite being sedated during the angiogram, I was surprised how much I remembered and experienced. I recall being in the recovery ward when the cardiologist came to see me with the results. He asked if I wanted the good news or the bad news. I wanted the bad news first. The results of the angiogram proved that I had had a SCAD. It was a small tear in the CXOM, which he explained was a small artery at the back of the heart that supplies blood to the heart. The good news was that there didn't appear to be any permanent damage of the heart and if there was a small amount of damage, he was sure the other arteries would compensate for it. But he insisted that it would heal and that I didn't need any other treatment, apart from medication. Despite being told that I had had a heart attack, I felt like I had won the lottery

Although I was advised of the changes I'd have to make to my life for the next six weeks to ensure the repair of the tear, I was given the all-clear to travel to Indonesia only 18 days after my SCAD. No running, no driving, no strenuous exercise, no lifting, no bungee jumping (my cardiologist's sense of humour!!!). Only walking for the next six weeks. I was more than happy to comply, as I was going on a well-earned holiday, so was more than happy to sit by a pool and relax.

I was discharged a few days later and prescribed 25mg Metoprolol (beta blocker) and Cloplavix (dual anti-platelets), which I was told I would need to take for 12 months.

I enrolled in Cardiac Rehab but only went for two weeks, as I felt that it didn't really help me with planning my recovery. Instead, my private health insurance company provided free of charge a rehabilitation consultant (as I was admitted as a cardiac patient). The rehab consultant provided weekly phone sessions, which helped me enormously. We were able to plan my recovery programme and also my running programme. I was able to gain insight into the medication I was on and the effects it would have on me, i.e., why I felt tired more than usual due to the beta blocker. The phone sessions went from weekly to monthly for up to six months.

Despite life going back to normal routine, this didn't stop me from constantly thinking about what had happened to me and if it would happen again. I recall for those first six months I religiously monitored my heart rate. I'm not even sure what I was expecting to achieve by doing this. The Metoprolol took some getting used to. I was astounded with the vivid dreams I had when I first started taking it. This settled down after a month or so. I was surprised at how tired I felt but again, this settled down after a few months. It took me about six months before I told anybody (apart from family and a few friends and staff) what had happened. Living in a small country town, everybody had heard I had not been well, but I felt I couldn't tell anyone what had happened until I had come to terms with it myself. My family and staff wouldn't let me 'overdo' anything. I don't think I lifted anything heavy for 12 months, not because I couldn't, but because no one would let me!!! I researched SCAD as much as I could on Google. Thank goodness for the MAYO Clinic website. This site helped me understand what had happened and that I wasn't alone. It didn't help me understand why it happened to me.

I came off all my medication after 12 months. The Cloplavix was stopped at ten months, as I started to experience very heavy menstrual flow and become anaemic. My GP was concerned that being on blood thinning medication may have caused this. Although my cardiologist wasn't certain about this, he was happy for me to stop taking them and only to take 100mg Aspirin for life. I stopped the beta blocker after 12 months on direction from my last cardiologist visit. I was always a bit cautious in what activities I chose to do. Although I continued with my jogging, I did reduce the distance and amount I did. I still played netball but didn't push myself physically like I used to. I was always a bit hesitant to exercise hard so that I was left breathless.

All changed for me about 18 months ago when I happened to speak to a cardiologist who had worked with Dr Jacqueline Saw (Renowned Cardiologist at Vancouver General Hospital and is the principal investigator of SCAD Research). He explained that, in his opinion, exercise like running was the right sort of exercise to do and that I should consider going back to my usual distance and frequency I was doing before my SCAD. He suggested that the only exercise I should avoid is lifting very heavy weights (not in my usual exercise regime anyway). This gave me the confidence to go back to my usual running regime and listen to my body to gauge if I was doing too much.

Now, three years post-SCAD, I've stopped asking why or why me. It doesn't consume my life as it did those first 6–12 months. I've run in a number of long-distance fun runs, including the Sydney City2Surf (my favourite fun run). I'm just happy to be able to live life normally (well, almost, made the decision no more half marathons). I'm back to my 'old self'. I have reassessed what's important in my life and now make decisions that are not going to put me under more stress (mentally or physically) than necessary. I'm enjoying life more and getting back to my adventurous self. (New motto in life 'We're here for a good time, not a long time'). Recently, I made the decision to go tandem sky diving. It was the most exhilarating experience and it was the turning point for me and my mindset. The only time I have had a concern is when recently I had to have a surgical procedure and then an operation where I was going under anaesthetic. I discussed my concerns with the anaesthetist and he was extremely interested in my SCAD episode. He reassured me that as there was no major heart damage and I was healthy, going under anaesthetic would not put me at higher risk. He was right. All went well and I also think that I recovered well, as I felt confident and reassured.

Joining the SCAD Survivor Facebook group has been another big positive. Just knowing that there are others from all over Australia, from all walks of life that have had a SCAD, some so much more severe than mine, has made me feel I am definitely not alone and to be more open and accepting about my SCAD experience. I'm very excited about being a participant in the DNA study of SCAD survivors with the Victor Chang Institute. If some questions get answered though this study, it would be great but I'm just happy to contribute to anything that can shed light on why this happens.

Zannia Watson – 18th April 2016 – Aged 31

On 18th April 2016, I sat down to the dinner table with my husband, sister, brother and five-day-old baby daughter, sleeping nearby in her basinet. My husband, Steve, had made moussaka for dinner and there was a bottle of my favourite red wine to share, which I figured I could enjoy if I timed it right in between breastfeeds. It's funny, the little details you remember.

I had taken two bites and suddenly felt as if the knife had jumped off the table and stabbed me in the chest. I had enough time to look at Steve and say, "Chest pain, chest pain," before I was unresponsive. I don't think that I ever passed out but I was in so much pain that the effort to speak or move just seemed all too much. My family moved me to the lounge, called the ambulance and loosened my clothes. I remember telling Steve that I didn't want to die. His response was to slap me across the face and tell me to keep breathing. And so, I did.

I kept breathing when the ambulance arrived seven minutes later, while the paramedics struggled to get my cold and clammy body off the lounge, while my siblings tried to answer questions and look after the baby and while Steve grabbed my purse and raced ahead to the hospital. I remember hearing my precious little girl crying in the distance and I yelled out, "Don't feed her formula!"

I had a dream first pregnancy. I was one of those pregnant ladies that everyone else likes to hate, you know, the kind that never gets sick or puffy or awkward and still fits into most of her clothes and works right up until the end. I started maternity leave with four weeks to go, expecting that our little one would follow the family trend and arrive early. She didn't. I walked around and around and around the block for three weeks and once I ticked past my due date, I even tried running. Then finally, in the early hours of 12th April, my waters broke with a tiny little trickle. It was just enough to keep me in hospital, where I spent the remainder of the day on an exercise ball, trying to get labour to start naturally. The next morning, I was induced but I was still determined to do this with the least amount of intervention possible. It was not to be. By midday, things were not progressing and the midwives dialled up the medication. The rest of the afternoon is a hazy blur of pain and heat waves before Steve finally had enough and called up the anaesthetist to administer an epidural. Everything sped up after that and soon enough, it was time to push. Oh, how I pushed! Little Miss L was nearly there when she turned her head sideways at the last minute and got stuck. The room quickly filled with medical staff and Steve put his hand over my eyes while they made cuts and scooped her out with forceps. And then there she was. Her Apgar score was very poor and she was whisked away for oxygen and assistance. All I could see were her tiny fingers holding Steve's hand. I didn't even know if she was a he or she yet! Two hours later, I was stitched back together, showered and flying high on adrenaline and Miss L was safely with her dadda in special care and I had my first real cuddle. Absolute bliss.

The next few days consisted of pure joy, unbearable pain, sleeplessness, slow trips down the hall to the special care ward, awkward attempts at breastfeeding and the never-ending rhythm of expressing every three hours. Miss L was hooked up to tubes for the first two days and fed by syringe, so she got it into her head that all she had to do was open her mouth and squeak like a little baby bird to be fed. We came home from hospital on the afternoon of 16th April, even though we still hadn't grasped breastfeeding. I had a great supply and had no trouble expressing, so I knew she was getting fed, but the midwife visits were stressful and, of course, everyone wanted a glimpse of our girl. I was exhausted and everything hurt but I was so overwhelmingly happy that everything else ceased to matter.

Finally, that afternoon, Miss L decided to latch and she fed for two hours straight. After that, I was disoriented, dizzy, had trouble following any conversation and focussing on my surroundings too an enormous amount of effort. As we were sitting down to dinner, I felt out of breath, as if I had run up a steep hill. When the pain hit, my first thought was a blood clot, because that was one thing we had been warned about when leaving the hospital. Then, in the back of the ambulance, I stared at the roof and thought to myself, *This is going to be really embarrassing when I get to the emergency room and they tell me I'm having a panic attack.* I never, ever imagined it would be my heart.

I don't think anyone in the emergency room imagined that either. They had wires and tubes and needles everywhere. I even had one stitched into my shoulder. I was freezing cold and kept yelling at them to warm me up. Steve told me later that the doctor had said he's felt corpses warmer than me. Someone must have hooked up an ECG as a precaution, because all of a sudden, that became the focus. I had a heart attack right there on the monitor. No one could believe what they were seeing but a CT scan revealed the LAD artery in my heart was 90% blocked. I was whisked with lights and sirens to another hospital and rushed into theatre for an angiogram. By this stage, they had filled me up with two full IV bags and I asked a nurse if I could pee. She barely looked at me. I asked again and the response was that I was about to be sedated. I lost it. With the last of my fading energy, I told her that I had just had a baby five days ago, was full of stitches where no one should have stitches and had been given more fluids than I could drink in a day and if they didn't get me a bedpan right now, I was going to pee all over the table. A bedpan magically arrived and I peed like I had never peed before.

I vaguely remember the doctor showing me the before and after scans of my heart and seeing the spot where they had inserted a biodegradable stent. Then I was in a dark room with wires all over my chest, a monitor that beeped incessantly and a husband that looked more like death than I did. I could barely squeeze his hand and he could barely keep his eyes open, except he was too afraid to close them. I slept lightly, the memory of the pain in my chest was too fresh to breathe deeply and the needles running up my arms were uncomfortable.

I spent a week in the CCU. I turned 32 and the nurses decorated my room with balloons and streamers. I was pushed all over the hospital for every test they could think of, and some of them twice. I had daily visits from Steve and Miss L and the nurses let them sneak in at all hours. They found me a breast pump from somewhere and Steve and the nurse worked it for me since my arms were still full of needles and tubes. When I was finally allowed to have a shower, Steve held my heart monitor out of the way while I tried to wash around the sticky pads and wires and post-birth blood. I remember apologising, saying that this was not what he had signed up for. He looked at me, naked and barely able to stand, and said, "This is exactly what I signed up for." We were just so glad I was still alive that nothing else seemed to register. At least, until the verdict came in. It took the doctors a few days but then they gave me a very long and rare condition. Postpartum Spontaneous Coronary Artery Dissection. All three layers of my artery had split open, the blood had clotted to plug the leak but then blocked the blood flow and triggered a heart attack. There were no warning signs, no family history, no risk factors, no reasons and no guarantees. I had very low blood pressure naturally and so, starting me on medication designed to lower my heart rate and blood pressure even further was a hit-and-miss endeavour, more often miss than hit. Hardest of all was the news that the meds were essentially poisoning my breastmilk and Miss L would need formula after all. I hadn't cried until then. Truthfully, that broke my heart far worse than the heart attack.

I returned home to a house full of family, a dead-tired husband and a baby that I didn't quite recognise. I returned home with deflated boobs and a hollow tummy and bone-thin thighs. I returned home, struggling to stand for more than a few minutes and unable to lift my little girl at all, not even to burp her. I was still feeling so blessed to be here at all but on the edges of that picture, there was also the growing realisation that everything had changed. The mother I had dreamed of being ceased to exist. When my parents returned home, Steve quit his job in the mines to stay home and care for us and I had a roster of church friends who came to sit with me a couple of times a week so Steve could leave the house to get groceries or go to the gym or just sleep. We sold our home for a fraction of its worth, packed up our life in Perth, carted our seven-week-old baby girl across the country and moved in with Steve's parents in NSW. We tried to pick up the pieces but for a long time, we both grieved and struggled to find our way through the debris. We blamed each other, because there wasn't anything else to blame and we railed against the unfairness of it all. If it hadn't been for an incredibly easy-going baby who greeted us with a huge smile each morning, I really don't know if we would have made it.

Now, as I sit writing my story, I am ten months on from my SCAD. Miss L is taking her first steps, cutting her ninth tooth, learning to sit on the potty, eating everything she can get her hands on and babbling a new word each day. And I am still so blessed to be here for each of these milestones. I struggle with my meds, I am black and blue all the time from the blood thinners and sometimes have to go back to bed after I take the heart rate tablets. I walk several kilometres every day and can lift my 12kg girl now with no trouble. I have about eight kilos to lose still and it is frustrating to see little children climbing the stairs at the beach easier than I can but I am trying to live within a new set of limits. My artery has completely healed and the stent has disappeared already. There is still damage to my heart but it is healing slowly. I do not know if I will be allowed to have any more children and I so badly want to give my little girl a sibling but I try not to worry about that just yet. We are still living with family and I long for a space of my own again, but this chapter is not forever. Steve has struggled to find full-time work close to home but we have just started our own patisserie business operating at the local farmer's markets and we are hopeful that this will pay the bills and give us the kind of balanced life that Miss L deserves with both her parents by her side.

This condition has cost me my health, my security, my faith in my own body, my dearly beloved job, my confidence as a mother, my home, my friends, my independence and, very nearly, my husband and the life I dreamed that we would have as a family. I miss my old self sometimes and I grieve anew when I am reminded of some aspect of the life I used to live before. This new body is often difficult to recognise and I am yet to trust it again.

But for each thing my SCAD has taken away, it has given me a gift in return. I am more patient than I ever dreamed possible. I am more affectionate, understanding and much slower to judge. I take more time to enjoy the company of family and good friends. I treasure each moment with my baby girl and I thank God each day for my husband who saved my life and makes it worth living. I leave the dishes and the laundry on a regular basis and go sit on the swings at the park with my little family. While my heart may yet be weak, my spine is forged from steel. I have an inner core that is so much stronger that I ever knew and a faith in God that is unshakable.

If He allowed my heart to break, and break almost it did, then surely, He will be the one to mend it once more. I know beyond any doubt that I am still here for a reason and that each day is a miracle. My story is not done; in fact, it is really just beginning. And so is yours.

From one heart to another, with love from Zannia. xox

Yvonne Hemmett – 2016 – Aged 43

I suffered two SCAD attacks this year (2016). The first one happened at work, I suddenly felt 'off'. Seconds later, had simultaneous pain running down both my arms to the end of my elbows and I started to get the shakes. I told my superior I didn't feel right at all and I've never felt like this before, which was not like me. All I wanted to do was go quietly in the empty meeting room to rest, thinking it'll pass, but my colleagues had called an ambulance thankfully. By the time they arrived, I was in considerable pain, which I was trying to keep to myself. I was more worried about freaking out my work colleagues, as my superior was on heart pills and my other colleague's wife had cancer, so he had a lot of stress issues of his own. I'm not one to make a lot of noise, as it seems to use more energy and freak everyone around you out. I was, however, rolling around on the floor in a foetal position, trying to rid the pain, just hoping, praying it would go away, as it was excruciating and my shakes were becoming overwhelming too.

First thing the paramedics did besides taking my blood pressure and pulse on my finger was give me glucose. The attack made my sugar levels drop and were too low, hence why I had the shakes. They then raided my work colleague's chocolate and fruit stashes to build up my sugar levels. This helped calm my shakes. The pain in my arms and chest did not fade though.

I recently separated and have endured a tremendous amount of stress as a direct result, which I knew. I thought I took the necessary precautions by seeing a counsellor for my children and myself. I love my work, so I was shocked this attack occurred at work, my safe zone, away from all my stress. I was wrong.

I disclosed this to the ambos but they seemed to think this attack was just an anxiety attack and recommended I go to my GP tomorrow, tell him what happened and ask my GP to do a blood test.

My arms were so painful and heavy (like from a nasty cramp), I couldn't even carry my handbag, let alone be able to drive home. I rang my brother to come pick me up to take me home.

I made an immediate doctor appointment for the next day to see my regular GP, told him of yesterday's events and that the ambulance people told me to get a blood test. My doctor, who I have seen for 14 years and knows of my personal circumstances my children and I have suffered from my ex-partner, said not to worry about the blood test, it was unnecessary and wrote me prescription for Aropax. I reiterated to my doctor that my arms were still really painful and that I am unable to even carry anything still. He just said I'd feel better in about 5–7 days once I start taking the Aropax but the pills will make me feel sick for the first week. Again, I said, "My arms feel like I've been bitten by a redback spider." He just told me to come back in about a week if I still feel unwell.

I went back home with my mum, who had to drive me to and from the doctors. Only a few hours after going home, another painful attack hit again. My parents were with me at my house, as they were worried about me from the day before. The ambulance was called. Again, tests were done and they kept saying I was having an anxiety attack. This time, I demanded they take me to hospital. I've had five kids, this pain I was experiencing was so painful, childbirth didn't even come close.

I was dosed up on Tramadol, morphine, etc., at the hospital and it made no difference. But I kept getting dismissed that I was suffering an anxiety attack or perhaps "Taki Subo", aka Broken Heart Syndrome. But I didn't have this. They kept leaving me, saying they had to attend other patients who were having major heart attacks. They made me feel like I shouldn't be in emergency. I was getting frustrated and annoyed. I just wanted this pain to go, but it didn't. The drugs did nothing. Finally, my blood tests came back, showing enzymes had been released to show my heart was in distress. Only then did this change their thought process. Then they moved me to the cardiac ward.

I had an angiogram and the head cardiac surgeon told me how lucky I was to get to hospital, as my LAD had dissected stopping my blood flow, hence my excruciating pain. The cardiac surgeon, Dr John Spiro, said it was my body shutting down. Not something you want to hear. He had to place two stents to mend the damage.

My cholesterol and blood pressure were all good prior to the attack, during the attack and after. Apparently, my arteries also appeared in good condition, which is why this was unusual.

I am 43, mother of five, whose overall fitness is reasonably good. I look healthy, so no one thought I'd be a candidate for having a major heart attack. I now have two stents in my heart. After having the two attacks, my heart pump was traumatised and the bottom part stopped working/pumping. I'm on a stronger dose of pills to slow my heart rate down to allow for my heart pump to start functioning properly again. As it is the bottom part of my pump, the doctor said they need to ensure the blood will still circulate fine in the meantime; otherwise, it could suffer a stroke. My specialist conducted various tests and was confident I would be okay. I did physical rehab at the hospital gym for eight weeks, which I enjoyed and gave me some confidence back and the results were also reassuring. Not happy taking pills for the rest of my life, as I can't afford to miss any with my life depending on them. I don't have a great memory, so remembering to take pills sucks. I hate taking pills unless I really have to, but now I have no choice.

If it wasn't for my insistence to take me to the hospital the second time, I'd be dead. We don't need a death to happen for the medical industry to take note. They need to be educated and think outside the box that everyone's body is different, as well as not be so close minded if a patient doesn't fit into their category of known diagnosis checklists of being overweight, old, heredity.

Marianne Punshon – 17th July 2014 – Aged 68

I sometimes think my SCAD was unusual, even for an unusual form of heart attack. SCAD patients are most often women without other heart disease risk factors, such as family history, being overweight or a smoker, or having high blood pressure and cholesterol problems. SCADs occur mostly in young, healthy, active, post-partum women, who may be about to menstruate. A link to history of migraine is being investigated.

I was aware of the possibility of heart attack, as my father had died from one at 58 years old, and my family history for many generations is polka-dotted with heart attacks as a cause of death in both the maternal and paternal lines. This was one strong risk factor I had.

My weight has always been a bit of an issue, but I have been overweight rather than obese. I was never a great fan of exercise but kept active and enjoyed gardening and going for walks. Both of my siblings have had issues with blood pressure, and although mine had been slightly elevated, it was controlled by medication. My cholesterol levels have never been of concern, and the only problem with my diet was that I ate too much of too many good things. I have never been a smoker. All in all, I had a couple of half-or-maybe risk factors for a heart attack unlike a person who suffers a SCAD.

In July 2014, I was feeling fitter and healthier than I had for a long time. Aged 68 years, I was enjoying my retirement, my family, my garden, my friends and my research into my family history. I had lost twelve kilograms in the previous twelve months and was attending a weekly exercise session and clinical Pilates class. Life was good. Was I starting to fit the profile for SCAD? Fit and active? Umm... Healthy? Probably. Young? Not! Post-partum? Not for many, many years. About to menstruate? Not for years. I didn't fit the typical criteria.

On the night of 16th July, I felt tired enough to go to bed early and read a book. My husband was unwell at the time. Suspected of having pneumonia, he was due to have scans and x-rays over the next two days. I was concerned about him but not overly stressed. The book I was reading was called *The History of Perthshire* and it related to my family history. Given what happened, it was obviously more riveting, stimulating and heart-grabbing than its demure title suggests!

I cannot put the events that followed into a precise timeframe, but between about 9pm and midnight, I suffered a SCAD and was admitted to hospital.

It is hard to define how it happened, but I remember feeling 'not right'. I was slightly nauseous and had mild headache, as well as a bit of a jaw ache, but it was nothing unusual that could not be put down to chronic sinus and a rumbly tummy. The jaw ache intensified, but this was still not unusual. Then I needed to rush to the toilet and started feeling a bit hot and clammy. I walked into the lounge room to tell my husband I felt strange and I thought something might be wrong. After that, I went back to bed.

There was a slight pain in my right shoulder. Then I felt a flat, smooth rock sitting just under the skin of my chest below my left shoulder. It fitted perfectly under my collarbone. In my mind, I could see the shape of it, and I remember feeling around for the large flat mass that didn't seem to exist and wondering where had it come from. By now, I was getting a little anxious and knew something was wrong. *Perhaps I had twisted my shoulder awkwardly?*

The next thing I felt was a whoosh as a wave washed over me from my chest to the top of head. Pain started in the left side of my chest. It was not acute but worrisome. In somewhat disbelief, I told my husband I thought I might be having a heart attack. The pain spread down my left arm, and I realised that it really was possible I was having a heart attack, even though I still didn't believe it. Heart attacks didn't happen like this – except I knew that they did. A few years earlier, a friend had circulated an email that listed the symptoms women feel when they have a heart attack. I was having all of them, or at least all those I could remember from that list. I couldn't deny it any longer. I was having a heart attack.

I called Nurse-in-the-Home and told her what was happening. She called an ambulance, which seemed to arrive in seconds. Two young men charged into my bedroom with their suction discs, coloured leads and clever machines that pronounced I was indeed having a heart attack. Protocol required them to call a MICA (mobile intensive care ambulance). As with the first ambulance, the MICA seemed to arrive very quickly, and two more young men joined the bedroom invasion, bringing with them more suction discs, more wires and more machines. I couldn't help wondering how they knew which wires went to which machines.

By now, the diagnosis of a heart attack was beyond any doubt. The ambulance officers talked to my husband. He was unable to drive at night, so they said he could accompany them in the ambulance. Knowing he was unwell, I said no. The ambulance officer replied that he wasn't going there, and I remember thinking that he must have thought I didn't want John with me. I most certainly did want his reassuring presence, but I was concerned about him going out on a cold night, as I was wheel-chaired down the seventeen steps from the front door to the driveway, to be ushered into the waiting ambulance.

In the emergency room, I was hooked up to more suction discs, wires and machines. There were blood tests and signatures – here and there, and this one too. I know I was told what all the papers I was signing were, but really, I had no idea. I remember a nurse telling me the time just after midnight as she attached another set of suction discs to me. She reassured me that I was okay and in the coronary care unit of the hospital. I was remarkably calm through the whole process. I knew I'd had a heart attack, but so did the paramedics and doctors and nurses, and I figured they knew what to do about it. I knew I wasn't going to die – not yet! All I wanted to do was sleep. Later, I was informed that I had suffered a spontaneous dissection of the left ventricle, a SCAD. This has since been medically managed.

Two and half years on, I enjoy my retirement, my family, my garden, my friends and my research into my family history. I joke about the night four handsome young men charged into my bedroom. I have regained some of the weight I lost, and I know I need to exercise more consistently. I intend to live for at least twenty years more and to dance at my grandson's 21st birthday. But always in the back of mind is that little acronym SCAD. Every time I get overtired or have a jaw ache or a sinus headache or sore shoulder or I start believing the unfounded, absurd and totally irrational idea that if I exercise too much or get too healthy, the fear arises that it might happen again.

Cathran Bowyer – 22nd April 2016 – Aged 65

My SCAD story happened in April 2016, a month before my 66th birthday. I'd been under a lot of stress, looking after ageing parents, but was otherwise healthy with low cholesterol, normal blood pressure, not overweight and fairly fit.

I had an angiogram in 2013 for stress-induced angina, which came back negative for blockages.

My story might give you a bit of a giggle.

I had put on a bit of weight but wanted to wear a particular pair of jeans. No worries I thought, I will put them on and do some stretches, toe touching, breathing in and holding it while I strained out. I repeated this movement several times.

That did the trick! The jeans now fitted but I immediately had a SCAD heart attack. Pains straight through arms, neck and chest, I felt nauseous and needed to rush to the loo. David rushed me into the local ED, where I had another heart attack, this time a STEMI on the bed!

I was given clot-busting drugs and rushed to the nearest big hospital. I should have flown but the plane had just left with another emergency patient. The road journey took two and a half hours and I was sure I was going to die on the way. I didn't, and the catheter discovered a tear in a branch of the right coronary artery and it was treated medically. The funny thing was it was touch and go until they swapped ambulances on route. The driver of the second ambulance sped off over a speed hump and my heart went back into sinus rhythm. It must have stuck the flap back in place, because I immediately felt better. I told the waiting team how it had happened and they were trying to keep a straight face! They said I had performed a Valsalva movement, which is the worst thing you can do for rushing blood through delicate arteries!

Next time I saw the cardiologist, he asked if I'd bought bigger jeans! I said, "No, I've just lost weight!" Cheeky devil!

I'm only a size 10, so I don't think I was being too ambitious! I also told him not to write a paper on tight jeans causing heart attack!

I spent five days in the Coronary Care Unit, being carefully monitored at all times. Upon discharge, I was given the usual meds, Plavix, a statin, BP drug and Aspirin. It took a while to get the meds sorted. I found I couldn't tolerate the Plavix or the statin, so my GP consulted the Mayo Clinic protocol for non-stented patients and stopped the Plavix and statin. I continued with the BP medication and 100mg Aspirin.

I started cardio rehab about three weeks after my heart attack and this really helped with my confidence. I also attended counselling sessions for Post-Traumatic Stress Disorder, which was invaluable in dealing with the aftermath of the heart attack.

A year on and I'm going well. I had a few trips to emergency with false alarms but got used to the new normal for me. At my one-year check-up, my cardiologist reported my heart had normal function. He attributes my ongoing angina upon exertion to Micro Vascular Disease and I'm being treated for that as a separate issue from SCAD. Looking back, I think I've been suffering from this for quite a few years before SCAD. I haven't been tested for FMD.

I belong to the Australian SCAD Survivors Facebook group and the worldwide SCAD Facebook group. These groups have been invaluable for my sanity and peace of mind.

Living in a small community has given me the chance to educate people about SCAD and I feel secure in the fact that the local emergency department is aware of my condition and wouldn't hesitate to consult the experts at the nearest large hospital. We also have a wonderful air ambulance service.

Fiona Ashworth – 21st June 2016 – Aged 48

I am a 49-year-old registered nurse with two teenagers. I am fairly active and wasn't on any medication with any past medical history. I don't drink or smoke either. I had never heard of SCAD until June 2016.

My colleagues at work didn't know anything regarding SCAD, apart from the doctors who knew about it from their medical training.

I had been busy at work until the early hours and had the next day off work. Whilst relaxing on the sofa, I felt a sudden pain in my chest, more like indigestion. I sometimes suffered from this, so to try and relieve it, I mopped the floor and drank some apple cider vinegar. This did very little. As this was the only symptom, I thought this can't possibly be a heart attack. When googling heartburn, heart attack kept appearing.

I lunched with my daughter but only felt like some peppermint tea. It seemed to feel better.

After grocery shopping, I carried the heavy bags in and it made the pain worse, but only when lifting the bags.

I spent an uncomfortable evening watching TV, then had some paracetamol, as we had no Aspirin, and went to bed.

It was still there early morning, so I rang the health helpline, who phoned an ambulance for me. I still didn't think it would be anything.

I walked out to the ambulance and the paramedics asked me if I was the patient.

As soon as they put the monitor on me, it was obvious I was having a heart attack. Immediately, they took me to the hospital, which confirmed I'd suffered a SCAD. No stent was required, so they treated me medically. My Echo indicated all my other coronaries were normal. Still they do not know the cause.

Cardiac Rehab was very informative and helped me get back to the gym.

Unfortunately, they can't say whether it will happen again or not, but I don't let that thought rule my life.

Sharon Kelly – 12th December 2016 – aged 41

Looking back to the day before my SCAD, I think of how happy I felt. I had not long turned 41 and had recently given birth to my third son, James, who was just ten days old. A girl friend had visited that day and we had sat for a few hours, chatting away and enjoying James and I remember saying to her how together I felt and that motherhood was coming to me much easier this time around.

Having a family has not come without a lot of heartbreak for my husband, Brett, and I. After a couple of miscarriages and a molar pregnancy, we finally fell pregnant with our first son, Benjamin, after three rounds of IVF. Ben was born via emergency caesarean at 36 weeks; however, our joy tragically turned to grief when we lost him two hours after birth. We subsequently learned that he had a rare genetic condition called X-Linked Myotubular Myopathy, which is not compatible with life for males and for which I am a carrier. This meant that we had to start the IVF process all over again but this time with a genetic component to add to the complexity. Our grief turned to joy following the birth of our rainbow baby boy, William, in November 2014. All of my children have been by caesarean.

My SCAD occurred in the early hours of 12th December 2016.

I had only been home from hospital four days when I woke just after midnight with what I would describe as a heartburn feeling in my chest. I had just had my first Lite n' Easy meal for dinner the night prior, so thought it might have been something in the meal that wasn't sitting right. The pain though was enough to wake me and make me sit up. I remember looking at the clock and thinking that I had a few hours until the next feed and wished that the pain would pass quickly. It didn't and soon I had some discomfort between my shoulder blades and a sudden feeling that I wanted to be sick. I got out of bed and went to the bathroom to be sick and then went to the kitchen and took a couple of Panadols and went and sat back on the bed. The pain in my chest was now becoming unbearable, an incredible pressure, and then the pain started to spread along my jaw. I looked over to my husband who was sound asleep and wondered if I should wake him. Sleep is so precious when you have a newborn and I honestly thought it would subside. After about ten minutes of this excruciating pain, I did wake him but that was only because by then I had pain going down my left arm, which I knew was not a good thing. He immediately called the ambulance, which at the time I thought was a bit melodramatic, but I went with it. Worst case, I thought I might have had a post-op clot from the caesarean, but at no time did I think it was a heart attack!

When the ambulance arrived, just after 1am, they were very quick in doing an ECG and getting me to put a GTN tablet under my tongue. The ECG showed only a slight irregularity but they wanted to take me to hospital for a full assessment. I really did feel like the paramedics and my husband were being a bit over the top with wanting me to go to hospital; however, I begrudgingly agreed to go on the basis that I could be there, assessed and back home in a couple of hours, as I had a newborn photoshoot booked for the following morning that I couldn't reschedule.

On arrival at the Emergency Department, the pain had completely gone. Bloods were taken and I was hooked up to monitoring devices. There, I just laid and waited and texted my husband with updates as I had them and told him I would just get a cab home when I was discharged, so he didn't have to wake the boys. A repeat blood test was done a couple of hours later, after which a doctor came and sat down next to me and told me that much to their surprise, my troponin levels had tripled and that meant that I had had a cardiac event and needed to be admitted to the cardiac ward.

What? The cardiac ward? No taxi home, no newborn photoshoot for me.

Over the course of the next couple of hours, I frequently heard myself being referred to as the "41-year-old female, ten days post-partem" and got a real sense of urgency from the medical staff. By 11am, I was being prepped for an angiogram (fortunately, through my wrist and not my groin). All this time, I was alone and still texting my husband. It was all so surreal and I had not grasped the severity of the situation.

I was awake during the angiogram and it was during the procedure that the cardiologist leant over to me and explained that I'd had a cardiac event and there was a 3-cm tear in my circumflex artery. This tear could not be treated by a stent or balloon, as it could possibly tear further, so I would be treated with medication.

Over the course of the next five days, I was on bed rest in the cardiac ward and closely monitored. My husband and I had agreed not to bring James into the hospital, although I missed him desperately. I cried continuously and couldn't believe what was happening. The word 'dissection' was used a lot but I really didn't know what it all meant. Cardiac issues were not in my family and it was not like I was surrounded by the jargon that was used on a daily basis. I knew that I had suffered a SCAD and that it was a rare condition believed to affect some women post birth but that was pretty much it. On the day of discharge, I was told in summary that I had to take things really gently, not to lift my toddler at all, not to walk up hills and any walks could be no longer than five minutes. I was given a list of medications that I needed to take and an appointment with my cardiologist for six weeks' time.

Unfortunately, I ended up back in emergency 12 hours later with another heart attack as I didn't do as was asked and took myself shopping for my Christmas present on the way home from hospital. This time, back in the cardiac ward, they were a lot firmer with me. I recall the cardiologist saying to me that he thought it might happen again, which was a piece of information that I would have appreciated. I was on complete bed rest and had to negotiate with the nursing staff to be allowed to have a shower with a compromise of a seated shower. Another five days later and with a lot of negotiation (also a few days before Christmas), I was allowed to go home. This time very aware of how serious my health situation was.

At the time, I went through a whole spectrum of emotions. Denial at what was happening but more so anger and sadness. Why? I wasn't your typical cardiac patient and certainly not in the age bracket (or so I thought) for it. A lot of tears were shed in the coming months and a hint of anxiety that it might happen again.

I had grand plans for myself whilst being on maternity leave this time and this included a vigorous exercise programme to get my body back to my pre-baby shape. This, of course, all went out the window. I did attend a rehabilitation programme through the hospital in the new year, which was a great way to get me back to gentle exercise in a supervised forum.

Almost six months on and nearly time for my next cardiologist review, I am feeling a lot better and hoping to reduce the number of medications I am on. To look to the positive side of things, it has changed me as a person. I am so much more calm, appreciative and grateful. I don't sweat the small things like I used to. I look at my sons with new eyes and a love greater than no other. I know I am a better mother because I am meant to be here.

Deborah Hubbard – 24th January 2017 – Aged 55

I believe my story commences in January 2017.

I had severe abdominal pain all day and night and was medicating myself with Nurofen during the day every four hours or less and Codeine at night. I couldn't lie on my left side and every night, I was pacing up and down the hallway in excruciating pain.

I had numerous trips to the doctor, who couldn't work out what the problem was. A multitude of tests began with the all-clear.

I presented to A and E one night, as I didn't think I could cope any longer! I was told that unless I had a life-threating issue, they would get the pain under control and send me home. I was physically and mentally exhausted.

The next week, I collapsed at work as the abdominal pain was not easing off with medication. Off to hospital and once again told the same thing, "We will get your pain under control and you will be released." The doctor asked if there was any problem at home or at work!!! He prescribed Amitriptyline Hydrochloride. The pain continued throughout the coming days and nights.

Looking back, I don't know how I managed but I remember feeling completely alone, let down with the medical profession, as no one really took it seriously and no one really understands what I'm going through.

Four days later, on 24th April, walking inside the house, I felt an awful pain in my chest, as I hadn't eaten any dinner as I wasn't hungry, so just thought it may be indigestion, so I sipped some soda water, with no relief.

The pain was intensifying, so I thought I would lay down upstairs to see if that helped, but it didn't, it was a crushing pain in my chest with pain down both arms. I was trying to calm myself and breathe into the pain but the thoughts of *I'm having a heart attack* kept overcoming me and I was trying to reason with myself that it's just not possible as I'm not a likely candidate for one. The minutes were ticking away and I knew that time was critical if I was having a heart attack. I thought, *I am going to die here alone.* I then just owned that fact that this was indeed the case and called Health Direct. I called them because I was also scared of calling an ambulance and going to the same hospital with the feeling of them thinking 'not her again'!

Health Direct immediately called the ambulance and they asked that I stay on the line and instructed me to get downstairs and unlock the door.

I then sat on the couch and called my partner with "get home quick", as that was all I could muster enough strength to say. I now realise exactly the magnitude of that call, he had no idea of what to expect when he arrived home.

The paramedics arrived and, thankfully, off I went to Sir Charles Gairdner Hospital. Once I was taken into resus (resuscitation ward), tests and bloods were taken, a young doctor spoke to me and said, "It appears you may have had a mild heart attack, but I think you may just have inflammation and you will most likely go home after four hours." After four hours, there was definitely a change in pace with the staff. Once they were sure that I didn't have any pain at all, they transferred me to Coronary Care Unit.

Majority of the time I couldn't fault the care or support I received. The only problem for me was with the night staff and after three days, the abdominal pain returned and no one seemed to really care about that as I was in the heart unit and at one time, I was told that that's not their concern as "you're here for your heart". I felt like I was back to square one and *what the hell am I going to do now!!!*

After two nights of walking the floor and crying in chronic pain, I finally received some strong pain relief. I am sensitive to morphine but I feel like if I end up in hospital again, with anything related to the artery condition I have, I won't tell them so I can get the pain under control more quickly.

I was shocked when I was told about SCAD of the circumflex artery (heart). The cardiologist and the registrar would say I was complicated due to the findings of irregularity of the distal cervical segment of the right ICA consistent with dissection (two neck artery dissections), one being the internal carotid artery. They then informed me that I have Fibromuscular Dysplasia in my kidneys and possible Mesenteric Ischemia of the gut that still needs to be investigated, which can lead to dissection.

I couldn't process all this information, so my partner, John, was present at all the morning doctor rounds. I was on various medications that my body didn't like, so I was either feeling nauseous or doped up. I felt like I was taking a cocktail of drugs and kept asking, "Are you sure I can take all these tablets together?"

On the evening of the 9th day, I was discharged, and leaving the hospital, I felt like my safety net was gone and I was worried.

I returned to A and E on the 17th May with a two-day headache and stabbing pain in my kidney. I was advised to take my medical information with me as if I mentioned SCAD, I may receive looks of 'what is that', which I did. I handed over the paperwork and was taken in quite quickly. I only went there as I was worried about the artery to my kidney, but the doctor was more concerned with my headache. After tests, six hours later and a good chat with a well-informed doctor, I was able to go home.

It really rocked me as a strong and confident woman and has left me feeling vulnerable and worried what the future holds. At times, I feel sadness and anger and then I feel grateful that I have experienced SCAD three times – two I don't know had happened and I'm still here living! I have always appreciated life and the beauty around me, so I will continue to do so even more so now. I need time to process and time will heal, although I know that I need to think about moving that piece of furniture or carrying all the grocery bags in from the car. My partner, John, has endured a lot of stress during and after, as he thought he may lose me and that made him become unwell for a short period of time. It has been incredibly hard for the family, as having to face uncertainty is difficult.

Not long after being at home, I received a call from Tricia, the Patient Educator for Cardiac Rehabilitation at Sir James Gairdner Hospital, and I cannot describe how much that call meant to me, somebody actually cares about me now I have left the hospital. If I am worried at all, I can call Tricia and get her advice and she will call me to let me know that appointments are being made and to check in and see how I am.

I am still trying to work out when to go to the hospital if I'm worried, I have felt unwell for a few days, with tightening in my throat and a hollow feeling in my chest and ended calling my nurse, LOL. I need to find a GP that knows about SCAD and the other conditions I have, as I'm complicated!

I have not had any abdominal pain since, but the theory is that the dissection may have healed now!

I'm due to commence the Cardiac Rehabilitation Programme and further tests all coming up within the next month. I am now forgetful and wondering if that's the medication.

I joined the Facebook group set up by Pamela McKenzie and know that I'm not alone.

Thanks to Pamela, I am able to tell my story, as the information you receive in hospital is generic for heart patients and there wasn't anything specific for SCAD. While I was in hospital, my family and I googled the condition and discussed it with each other, as that was the only info we could get.

Also, with the amazing efforts of Pamela, I hope that the medical world understands SCAD. I am able to participate in the Victor Chang Cardiac Research Institute in the genetics of Spontaneous Coronary Artery Dissection. I feel this gives me reasoning as to why this happened to me, to help and educate others about SCAD.

Patricia Bunu – 2nd August 2015 – Aged 43

My name is Patricia Bunu and I am of African descent. I classify myself as fit, active and medium-sized lady. With more than 20 years of nursing experience from Australia and Zimbabwe, I had never heard of SCAD until 2nd August 2015 when I was a victim.

After having a good vacation in Africa, I had just landed back in Perth around 4pm and went to bed a bit early on the day, as I was feeling very tired. Around 9pm, I woke up feeling nauseous, so I got up to go to the bathroom but could not vomit.

As I was walking back to the bed, that is when I felt a very sharp pain on my chest, shortness of breath. Clammy and I knew something was really wrong. I could not walk back to bed, so I knelt down and asked my husband to call the ambulance. He thought I was just really tired and asked me to take some Panadol and come back to bed. I told him to switch on the lights and call our daughter so she could come and check my blood pressure.

My husband jumped out of bed and assisted me back into our bed. When my daughter came in, she checked my blood pressure and it was 160/80. She rang the ambulance, which arrived in no time. The paramedics administered GTN spray twice in five minutes' intervals and Aspirin 300mg and then the pain went away. They took an ECG, which indicated an acute myocardial infarction but they said the ECG tracing was normal.

They took me to hospital, where blood tests for troponin levels were done and came back positive. A second troponin came back higher than before and was told I had a heart attack. I never thought I would have a heart attack at the age of 43, furthermore, with no family history of myocardial infarction. The only trigger I suspected could have been the blood pressure medication I had been taking safely for the past 14 years. Following pregnancy-induced high blood pressure, I subjected to persistent postnatal hypertension.

I was admitted to CCU, where an angiogram was done and confirmed Spontaneous Coronary Artery dissection (SCAD). Luckily, I did not require stenting and was discharged home on a beta blocker, blood thinner and to continue taking blood pressure medications. I had dozens of questions, such as how, why, what if and most of my questions still remain unanswered, because the real cause of my heart attack is not known.

I am very grateful to the SCAD Facebook page which has answered some of my questions. One of the ladies in this group from Queensland rang me and we talked for a long time. She shared her story with me and it relieved all the anxiety I had. This is my story.

Tahnee Hohendorf – 4th July 2015 – Aged 33

I guess you could say my story started in 2009 when my sister suffered from multiple NSTEMI heart attacks resulting in a double bypass and was later diagnosed with SCAD. It was such a scary time for our whole family, as she very nearly didn't make it. Little did I know that her history would save my life six years later.

I had high blood pressure throughout my first pregnancy in 2011 and then after my second was born in 2013 and again towards the end of my twin pregnancy in 2015. I gave birth to the twins naturally and around that time, I had influenza and was coughing continuously for about eight weeks.

When my babies were just eight days old, at around 3pm, I had what I thought was a pulled muscle across my shoulder blades (made sense with the coughing and recent childbirth). I took a Panadol and popped a heat pack onto it and the pain went away. In the early hours of the morning the next day, around 2am, I was woken up with the same pain. I tried the heat pack / Panadol again, but it didn't work. My awesome husband was sleeping at the other end of the house with the kids so I could recover from the birth and coughing and he brought the twins in for a feed. I told him the pulled muscle was hurting again, fed the babies, and he took them back to bed.

A couple of hours later, I actually googled heart attack symptoms but dismissed it, as there was no other pain besides across my shoulder blades. I rang 13HEALTH and described my symptoms and they said they would send out a doctor. It got to 6:30am and they still hadn't arrived. By this stage, I had pain in the tops of both arms and down my left arm. The doctor turned up just after 7am and gave me pain relief tablets that did nothing. By now, the pain in my left arm was so intense, I could barely speak. He said that my blood pressure was up and he would like me to go to the hospital. "No need for an ambulance," he said. So, I fed the twins (boy and girl), called my mother-in-law (who lives in our granny flat) to watch our other two kids (one-year-old daughter and three-year-old son) and my husband took me and the twins to the hospital. It was just after 8 by the time we got there.

I was still convinced that it was just a pulled muscle as they were doing any ECG. I kept telling my husband not to worry. It was at this point I told them about my sister's history and he exclaimed, "That's it!" I still didn't believe him. I was on morphine and asking them to keep the dosage low enough so I could feed the babies again. I fed my little girl and was halfway through feeding my little boy when they came in and said I needed a CT scan immediately. I stopped feeding my son, to go in right away. Had I known that would be the last time I would ever breastfeed again, I would have savoured the moment a little longer. This still upsets me when I think about it.

They took me in past a bewildered older lady who had been taken out so I could go in. They took me straight from CT scan to the cath lab for an angiogram. Still believing it was a pulled muscle, as they wheeled me past the nurse's station, one of them yelled out, "Troponin is 350." It was only then that I thought... *Crap. I've had a heart attack!*

I'll never forget them wheeling me past my husband and telling him to come and say goodbye with the babies. Watching him at the end of a hallway, looking so scared with our tiny babies in the pram as I was going in for surgery will be forever in my mind.

I watched the surgery and saw the tear right away. It was repaired with two stents end to end, 6cm all up. I was okay until they came up with blood thinning tablets and told me that I couldn't breastfeed any more. It was then that I cried uncontrollably. They were so tiny and I was now rendered useless (in my mind). It has taken a long time to be okay with it. It's now been two years and the twins are gorgeous and healthy. I didn't need to be worried but breastfeeding the twins was something I had really been looking forward to and it was taken from me when they were just nine days old. It wasn't fair!

I spent the next five days in CCU, recovering whilst also still coughing from the influenza, and trying to dry up my milk that I so desperately wanted to give to my babies. Amongst all of this, I also had an allergic reaction to the contrast dye. I must have looked a sight.

All in all, my ejection fraction went from 42 a year ago to 50 earlier this year. I am doing well and loving being here for my four gorgeous kids and amazing husband. It's still hard to comprehend and I still have bad days, but having my sister to talk to about it all has been a real help. If it wasn't for her, I don't know if they would have picked up what it was in time, as I had no risk factors. I've never smoked, never tried drugs, am not overweight and only drink occasionally. I was only 33 at the time too. Interestingly, the same age my sister was. The two heart attacks I had were the STEMI type and my cardiologist said I would not have survived a third. I owe her my life!

Thanks for reading my story, Tahnee

Jen O'Neill – 25th February 2016 – Aged 36

I had a SCAD heart attack on the 25th of February 2016. I was 36 years old at the time and I had an 11-month-old baby and a three-year-old toddler. In the lead up to my SCAD, I had been suffering from horrible stress. My three-year-old had been diagnosed with Autism a few months prior, so not only were we running around doing numerous therapies with him, I was also grieving from this diagnosis and the lifelong implications of this disability. My baby was also not sleeping, I was getting about three hours broken sleep a night since he was born. We had recently returned home from a week at Tresillian Sleep School in Sydney to try and help with this. I was breastfeeding at the time and had got my first period since giving birth the week prior to my SCAD.

At the exact time of my SCAD event, I was eating dinner and crying as I was telling my husband about my awful day. I felt a sharp pain in the side of my left breast. I assumed it must have been mastitis, as I was still breastfeeding. But then the pain went down my left arm. At this point, my husband – who is a police officer and had witnessed people having heart attacks previously – started to get concerned.

All of a sudden, I felt terribly sick and ran to the bathroom to vomit. The pain became a strong ache, but it persisted. My husband wanted to call an ambulance but I refused to let him. He called his parents over to look after the children and we left for the hospital. I was admitted straight into hospital due to my heart attack symptoms but was told it was most probably stress. They took a blood test and the treating doctor was surprised that my troponin levels were raised.

I was kept overnight for observation. In the morning, I was advised that I needed to have an ECG and an angiogram to rule out a heart attack. They performed an ECG quickly but the results were normal. I was starting to feel very anxious, as I needed to get home to my babies – in particular my littlest who was still being breastfed. I was told that I couldn't leave the hospital until I had an angiogram, and that may take 1–2 weeks as there were people who needed it more than me. I felt like a hypochondriac!

At this point, I became quite upset. I was sitting in a four-bed hospital ward, with sick elderly men, with my boobs out, pumping milk. I asked to be transferred to the private hospital and within a few days of transferring, I had an angiogram. Just before going in for the procedure, I was told that it was likely that nothing would be found in the angiogram – they believed perhaps stress had caused the pain. I 100% agreed with this. However, as I was laying down in the procedure, the cardiologist was shocked to find I had what looked like a spasm. However, I was given anti-spasm meds and it did not work. I could hear the nurses and doctor discussing what to do next. The cardiologist leant over and told me that it seems I did have a heart attack and that he had three choices – the first to stent me, but he did not wish to do this due to my age. The second was do nothing and seek advice. And the third was to have open-heart surgery. I began crying (whilst trying not to move because I had a wire in my body!). I remember saying, "But my baby isn't even 1!" A lovely nurse dabbed away my tears. He decided to seek advice and I was taken back up to the ward. After discussions with their colleagues in Sydney, I was advised that I'd had a Coronary Artery Dissection. I have no family history of heart disease, no high blood pressure or any concerns to do with the heart.

What a shock it was to learn that if my husband didn't take me to the hospital when he did, things may not have ended as well. The cardiologist said my husband saved my life by recognising the signs and rushing me to the hospital. I was in the hospital for eight days and was discharged on my littlest's 1st birthday. A day I will never forget. Unlike so many other mums that had suffered a fatal SCAD, my small boys still had their mum. I felt incredibly lucky but was still in shock.

Since having the SCAD, I have been medically managed and continue to take traditional heart meds, such as Amlodipine, Aspirin, Metoprolol and Clopidogrel. I see my cardiologist regularly. Emotionally, I still don't believe this horrible scare has sunk in. I have doubted my body and not trusted it to do exercise. I went through a period of anxiety and depression. But although I have been upset at times, I certainly don't feel like a 'victim' now. If anything, I feel stronger now, as my body has been pushed to its limits... and I survived! How amazing is that?

I am blessed to have an amazing support around me – my wonderful husband and sons, my parents and parents-in-law, not to mention my extended family who rallied around and helped us get through this time. For that, I will forever be grateful. The biggest lesson I have learnt from all this is to not stress about the little things. I have faith that things will be okay and that I have the strength and resilience that even a massive health scare couldn't take away. How blessed am I?

Bernadette Ravenwood – 25th March 2015 – Aged 36

My name is Bernadette, I have two children (5 and 11), am 38 years old and a SCAD survivor.

One late afternoon in March 2015, I was at work (in an office) when I experienced a sudden onset migraine of epic proportions. Although I have lived with migraines all my life, this one was different, I generally get warning signs, and it was accompanied by tightness in my chest and numbness in my arms. I took a few Aspirin and rested for half an hour before finishing my working day and going home.

Next day, I was tired and fuzzy but experienced no further symptoms, so I continued on as usual. At the time, I was working long hours under high pressure, and home life was emotionally very stressful. The following morning (again at work), I got a sudden crushing pain in my chest, with shortness of breath, achy pain in my arms to the elbows and numbness of my lower arms. Not knowing what was happening, but remembering the odd migraine from two days before, I went to my GP, in tears and terrified. They hooked me up to the ECG, which didn't show anything, and sent me to pathology for blood tests just in case. I was grateful to my GP for taking me seriously.

I received a call an hour later, saying I needed to have someone drive me to Emergency, as the blood tests showed very high levels of troponin. At the hospital, they tested again, showing greatly increasing troponin levels. I was hooked up to all the machines, had interns, residents and nurses in and out, asking whether I'd taken any drugs, more and more blood tests, questions and various standard heart attack medical treatments that had no effect. I was scared, tired and frustrated that no one could tell me what was happening. At 11pm, after eight hours in the Emergency department, I was moved to the cardiac ward. They still couldn't tell me what had happened – all the tests showed that a completely fit and healthy 36-year-old had suffered an NSTEMI for unknown reasons.

Waiting in the cardiac ward for an angiogram was a very isolating experience. I was the youngest person there by about 30 years. I couldn't sleep, couldn't think, couldn't focus and just internalised everything. I wanted to go home but didn't know if I was going to have another attack with a worse outcome.

Thirty-six hours later, I was taken to have an angiogram. One of the cardio nurses mentioned SCAD – she had read about it and thought what I had experienced sounded similar. I had never heard of it. The angiogram showed a healthy heart with a dissection of the left anterior descending artery. Thanks to muscle spasms, the angiogram was more painful than the heart attack. Luckily for me, the tear was in a good spot for full recovery without surgical intervention. I was put on the same drugs and doses as an 80-year-old with chronic heart disease, as they didn't know how to treat me. I was discharged a few days later with a suggestion of possible SCAD, no referrals, a few days off work, no rehab, no information.

A couple of weeks later, after a five-minute consult with the hospital cardiologist, feeling sick and depressed and getting stressed at every minor symptom, I went to my GP to request a private referral to a cardiologist. He was great – he had seen SCAD before, gave me lots of information and reduced the dosages of all the medications (stopping all of them after six months). On a subsequent visit, he confirmed I was physically in good shape, could recommence normal physical activity gradually and should be back to normal in a few months. He was right – physically I felt fine (other than a minor setback of a haemorrhagic cyst believed to be caused by the excessive blood thinner doses I had previously been on). The incessant tiredness only lasted about nine months, and I had returned to normal activity levels without rehab within six months.

The lasting effects have not been physical ones. I now suffer anxiety attacks (lessening in frequency and duration as time goes on), increased depression and wonder constantly if and when the next SCAD will happen and if it will be worse next time. However, discovering all the information on the

MAYO clinic and Victor Chang websites has helped a great deal with the worrying.

I have learnt to cope with stress better, to listen to my body and be a bit less demanding of myself. Finding the Australian SCAD Survivors Facebook group has been amazingly beneficial – hearing the stories, sharing fears, knowledge and experiences, supporting each other – has had a much greater effect on my psychological wellbeing than any other treatment. I have been so lucky – not only in recovery from SCAD, but in the support I have received and learnt to ask for. I have travelled overseas without incident, am coping well with kids, life and work, have raised awareness of SCAD amongst my family, friends, community and medical practitioners, and hope that sharing my story and participating in research will help others, as I have been helped.

Raelene Toms – 26th March 2016 – Aged 58

At the time of my episode, I was an active 58-year-old with no medical history. I walked each morning for an hour and was active in my job as a registered nurse in charge of the Transit Unit at Port Macquarie Base Hospital. My job could be a bit stressful at times and very demanding.

On the day of my event, I was on my days off, it was actually Easter Saturday, 26th March 2016. I had spent an uneventful day with my daughter Ti'arne, going out for breakfast, then shopping. I was a bit tired and had a nap for an hour in the afternoon. Upon rising, I organised our evening meal and set about preparing and cooking it with Ti'arne's help. Just as I was about to take the chicken wings out of the oven, I got the worst bout of indigestion imaginable. It was so bad that I rushed into our en-suite and vomited, I then got this really bad central chest pain and sweats. I thought the sweats was due to my vomiting, so I had a shower.

After my shower, I asked my daughter to drive me to the ED at the Port Macquarie Base Hospital, as the pain was not subsiding. On the way to the hospital, Ti'arne asked me if I wanted her to pull over several times, as the pain was not easing.

On arrival to the ED, I was triaged and taken straight in where I had my observations taken and then I was taken to a recuse bay. An ECG was recorded, which showed I had a STEMI. I had a cannula inserted and was thrombolysis which reverted my ECG changes back to normal, I also had an IV with morphine for the pain.

I was admitted to the CCU with continuous monitoring with the likelihood of being transferred to Prince of Wales Hospital Sydney. Saying goodbye to my husband and daughter that night with the belief that I would go to Sydney, have an angiogram and be back home the next day. At 3am, the CCU register advised me that I would be going down to Sydney as a second person as they had an urgent transfer who needed to have an angiogram as soon as possible. So, in the early hours of Easter Sunday, I was transferred down to Prince of Wales Hospital Sydney to their CCU with the critically ill man.

Arriving at Prince of Wales Sydney, I had my own room. I was informed that I would have an angiogram after the patient I came down with from Port Macquarie had his. At about 10am, I noticed the other patient I was transferred to Sydney with being wheeled past my room and also noticed him return.

The staff then came to collect me to have my angiogram. I was wheeled into the lab, where they inserted another large cannula for the procedure, explained to me what they were going to do and what to expect. I thought I underwent coronary catheterisation but on return to my room, my cardiologist came to visit me and told me they had found something that they were not expecting. I'd had an extensive spontaneous left main dissection extending to the distal LAD with non-obstructive disease elsewhere, which I, as a nurse, had never heard of. He also informed me that they were treating me conservatively as they did not want to operate on me unless it was the last option as I had a thrombolysis in Port Macquarie and I could bleed to death.

Subsequent to the angiogram, I experienced further chest pain with new ST elevation anteriorly. After my coronary angiogram, when I was going through my second bout of chest pain, my specialist enquired as when my husband would be arriving. I told him tomorrow or the next day. He insisted on me giving him Steve's contact details. Steve told me later that my cardiologist told him to make his way to Sydney as soon as possible, as I might not make it through the night. Steve was also told that surgery was his last option, as they might not be able to stop the bleeding.

I was managed medically with an IV of Heparin and Metoprolol, GTN infusion and Clopidogrel in context of my Aspirin allergy.

I had daily Echo of my heart and remained on strict bed rest for ten days. Upon leaving Prince of Wales Hospital, the cardiology registrar stated that I had no idea how sick I was, which, later, I acknowledged as the truth.

I was transferred back to Port Macquarie Base Hospital by air ambulance to the CCU and put on continuous monitoring. After a week, I was only allowed to be discharged home under the condition that I was not left alone.

I had the occasional twinge in my chest, which concerned me, so my cardiologist did a cardiac stress test on me and an Echo, which were both normal.

My entire family have been by my side the entire time, with my eldest daughter travelling form Port Hedland. Without their support and love, I didn't think I would be here today. It has been life changing for me and my outlooks on life have changed.

I had nine weeks off work and returned back to work on light duties, I was not allowed to do any heavy lifting or pushing for six months and had a weight gain of 10kgs, which, sadly, I'm still working at losing.

I'm due for my next check-up in September, where my cardiologist is going to give me a stress test and another cardiac echo.

I never thought I would get back to the level of fitness I had prior to my episode but I'm getting there slowly and now I have a much better appreciation of life, friends and family. Possessions are of little importance and life is precious and ends far too soon. Each day with my family is a blessing.

Helen Favelle – 8th April 2015

It was two years ago, Wednesday, 8th April 2015.

I had been to my usual after-work, Wednesday night swim squad and as I rode my bike home, I had pain in my chest as I rode up the hills. At home, I sat on the couch, chatting with my son and partner, and eating avocado on toast. I felt 'smashed' from the swim squad but pretty happy. I went to bed.

On Thursday, I rode my bike to work. As I went up a ramp to get onto the bridge across the river, the same pain happened in my chest. At work, a friend cancelled a coffee catch-up, so I used the time to make an appointment with my doctor of twenty-five years. My son drove in and picked me up, and dropped me at the doctors as I wanted to get back to work quickly. I told my doctor I had been given a flu vaccine earlier in the week, and I felt like I had the flu plus I had pain in my chest when riding my bike uphill. My doctor did an ECG and then told me that I needed to go to the hospital quickly. She asked my son to drive me there immediately as it was just around the corner.

At the hospital, they gave me a blood test, aspirin and a needle in my stomach. I had another ECG and an echocardiogram. I had never heard of troponin levels but apparently, my levels indicated I was having a heart attack! The cardiologist was perplexed as I had no heart disease history but he did say there is a very rare chance that a split forms in the artery and this may be the cause of my heart attack. I was admitted to hospital and was given nitrate and morphine that made me feel awful. I was booked in for an angiogram.

During Thursday night, my troponin levels went up so I was given even more morphine.

On Friday morning, I had the angiogram and I recall, through the haze of drugs, the cardiologist say it's the real McCoy, a SCAD in the lower branch of the circumflex. I also recall hearing the adjective 'pristine' used in reference to my arteries.

I was taken back to the ward and over the next week I was placed on beta-blockers, blood thinners and advised to rest. I booked into the cardio rehab program and was discharged. On the way home from the hospital, I recall thinking what the hell was that all about! It was all a bit much.

I went back to work for a few weeks but found that the drugs made me feel slow and fuzzy. I took a month off. I found scientific journal articles about SCAD and worked with my cardiologist over the next year to wean off the beta-blockers and blood thinners. I now only take a daily aspirin.

I joined the Facebook group and have filled out the surveys for the Victor Chang Institute study. I learned that most SCAD survivors were fit women, who like me, maybe suffered migraine.

In the year of my SCAD, my mother had been unwell (and passed away two months after my SCAD), my son had left home to do his country teaching service and I had started a new role at work. A fair amount of stress I suppose! I also had suffered from PMS and put it down to perimenopause. I had a hospital admission for pre-eclampsia during my pregnancy and bad migraines. I do think that my SCAD was caused by a combination of hormones and stress. I can control stress but it is a constant battle!

To celebrate my two SCAD anniversaries, I have taken cycling tours in New Zealand and I have continued to complete ocean swims that I train for at swim squad. I initially went back to work for four days a week however since February this year, I am back to five.

There is a lot to scare you about having a SCAD and I do sometimes think what if I had just gone to coffee with my friend and not to the doctor that day. However, I try to focus on the positive outcome I have had and look forward to many years of life ahead.

Lisa Dibdin – 3rd May 2016 – Aged 35

My name is Lisa. I have a wonderful supportive husband and two boys aged six and two. I was only thirty-four when my SCAD happened.

It was a usual morning of getting the kids ready for school and day care, before my late shift at the hospital. I worked there as a RN on the cardiac ward, which, looking back, is ironic!

It all started when I was bringing in two full baskets of washing from the garden. I was balancing the baskets on top of the other whilst opening the back door when I felt a twinging, burning sensation in my chest. I assumed the laundry basket had accidentally pushed into the centre of my chest, making it sore so I gave the area a rub and carried on with the washing. The pain, however, didn't subside and the burning feeling intensified.

My initial reaction was "Great, I've given myself indigestion now," as I've experienced that several times before. The burning sensation was like a horrific heartburn going from the centre of my chest straight down into my abdomen. For relief, I took some indigestion tablets with a bit of fizzy drink and did a burp which weakened the sensation. I then made an emergency doctor's appointment to get my 'heartburn' checked out.

Problem solved, I thought, however within five to six minutes, the burning pain was back again and it became really irritating and uncomfortable. I was supposed to be walking my oldest son and my neighbour's children to school that day and I started to wonder if I could make it. So, I sent my son over to my neighbour's house to tell her I had an awful pain in my chest. She came over immediately to check on me and

145

said I looked awful. I took more indigestion tablets with fizzy drink and proceeded to do several huge burps, which made me feel a lot better. My neighbour then took my oldest son to school whilst I got ready to drive my one-year-old to day care on route to see the doctor.

Before I could leave the house, the burning pain came back with a vengeance, I had to take my bra off as it felt like it was crushing me and making the symptoms worse. I rang my husband at work and asked him if he could drive me to the doctors and take our one-year-old son to day care. I told him I was getting quite scared of the burning pain as it wasn't quitting. His reply was "Phone an ambulance," to which I replied, "No it's not that bad, it's just really bad indigestion or oesophageal spasm or something." In hindsight, that is when I needed to phone 000 but as a medical professional, sometimes the person you least expect an emergency to happen to is yourself!

My husband told me he was fifteen minutes away and I was relieved. To help him, I thought I would put our son into the car seat so we could leave as soon as my husband arrived. This was not a good idea as when I lifted my 11kg son into our wagon, the pain ripped through my entire body like nothing I had ever experienced before, radiating down my back and neck. At this point, I was smart enough to realise that the hospital was the better choice so I cancelled the doctor's appointment and waited for my husband to arrive.

Once my husband came home and we set off, we had a big discussion in the car about which hospital to go to. To save time, I wanted to go to the local emergency department, get an ECG, get checked out, then come home. I still didn't think it was anything serious and didn't want to go to the larger hospital I worked at for fear that it was only indigestion. My husband had enough sense to completely ignore me and drove straight to the hospital where I work. I presented to triage with a burning sensation in my chest radiating through to my back, left arm and fingers. When triaged, I told the nurse that it was just a bit of indigestion and sent my husband off to drop off our son.

I waited for a short time before being taken to the small triage room for a 'quick' ECG to rule anything out. To my surprise, within seconds, I was being walked to an ED trolley with the ECG machine still attached and having my bloods taken. Now, being a cardiac nurse, I thought to myself that this was all a bit extreme. I had done a six month work placement in this emergency department a few years previously and I knew most of the nursing staff there as well – awkward.

One of the nurses I knew said, "We have a bed for you," to which my reply was, "Already? Awesome, am I going round to A-side?" Her answer was one I won't forget for a very long time, "Um no, straight to resus. You are having runs of VT and have a very nasty looking ECG reading." Ventricular tachycardia (VT) is a fast heart rhythm that originates from the ventricles; it doesn't always cause symptoms but it can also turn into ventricular fibrillation, which is an inadequate heart rhythm where upon your heart might stop and you go in to cardiac arrest.

I thought they were pulling my leg and giving me grief; I was sure it was a joke. I was rushed into the resuscitation room and a code blue was called and the room was filled with nurses, doctors and x-ray staff, all of whom I knew. Upon entering the room, they all looked at me, and I looked at them and time stood still as they checked the cardiac monitor above my head then back at me again. It was one of the most surreal experiences imaginable; here I was, being looked after as a patient when I was the one who was usually looking after others.

I had more bloods taken whilst being hooked up to every piece of medical equipment possible. The chest pain, back pain and left arm and numbness in my entire left hand was not reducing but continued to get worse. Just when I thought it couldn't get any more worse, in rushes the cardiologist from my ward upstairs; she looks at the monitor, grabs the ECG reading, frowns, then looks up to see me. Her face falls and she instantly requests that the defibrillation pads be put on.

That's when I knew I was in big trouble and that this wasn't some little weird ECG blip or indigestion related anything.

At this point, I said my prayers and asked to be watched over, kept safe and that my faith would stay strong throughout the ordeal, that I knew was about to occur. I kept up my sense of humour throughout the proceedings trying to lighten the mood for not just myself but the staff and colleagues around me.

Before I had really digested what was going on, I was being whisked off to the cath lab for an angiogram, a place I never thought I'd be a patient in. As all the patients I had taken down were either elderly, overweight, or had cardiovascular disease; I was none of those things. On the journey through the hospital, my heart kept going into runs of VT causing the monitor to alarm. I kept telling the nurse and doctor that it was a faulty machine or that the porter had gone over a bump to fast. I think that they were really struggling at this point to keep up the banter with me due to being so concerned about my safety.

Once in the cath lab, I insisted transferring myself over onto the bed and was just wondering if I would know these staff members too. Of course, it was the staff that I knew and who I transfer patients to regularly, and who also looked as shocked and concerned about seeing me on one of their beds instead of alongside of it.

It was very quiet in the cath lab and everyone was staring at the screen. I was also looking hard but couldn't see anything. That's when they pointed out the long tear down my left anterior descending (LAD) artery. I was then taken to the CCU ward upstairs where I was met with more staff that I knew and that were also having a hard time treating one of their own.

As I sat on the bed, the entire gravity of the situation descended on me. I had some really difficult phone calls to make. So, I rang a close friend and colleague who was currently on holiday from the hospital. I told her I was in CCU; the reply was "Lucky you, hope you have a good shift." She couldn't believe it when I told her I was the patient and had torn my LAD; she rushed straight over from having a coffee and brought me one too. It was great having someone to chat with about what I was going to tell my husband as that bothered me the most. As I had already put him through so much in the past when I had a brain tumour that needed removing and I was told that it was a risky surgery and they then found something wrong with the back of my brain and spine. It was one of the worst calls I had to make alongside the phone call to my mum in the UK where I had to tell her and my brother on his birthday that I possibly had what my dad had died of five years previously. He had a ruptured aorta that they tried to fix but it caused an aneurysm in his aortic arch to tear and he died before they could repair it. I was assuming that what I had was a similar thing.

My husband was great, he was so supportive and came in with a hot drink and some banter to throw at me. Our marriage is based on our strong faith, smiling, moving forward and giving each other as much fun grief as we can. We laughed, which gave me some momentary relief, and I was able to keep it together to make the phone call back home to my mum. This was an intensely difficult thing to do especially since I had such limited information to share with them at that point.

The rest of the day passed as a blur of tests, CT scans with dye, x-rays etc. It wasn't until later on in the evening that I was first told about SCAD. That word changed my life forever; now, looking back, not all necessarily bad but at the time, everything seemed pretty bleak.

The next morning, the tribe of cardiologists and nurses descended on my room, where they talked about how they had found three other aneurysms, two near my spleen, and one in my brain. They told me about SCAD; what it was and that they were unsure of the cause. They told me about the treatment and the restrictions that follow a SCAD.

This is where my whole life changed in that one conversation. No lifting over 10kg again ever, no heavy duty work again ever, no sudden increasing blood pressure or heart rate. I was so stunned and shocked that I stared blankly at them for what seemed like ages before I said, what about my son what about my job. My one year old was already 11kg and was only just walking. Also, there is no such thing as light duties on a cardiac ward and besides I was only on a contract not permanent that meant my contract would be terminated in less than three months when it was due for renewal.

I was told that to stay alive and prevent it from reoccurring that I would need to stick to these rules. I did something that I swore as a patient I would never do I was rude to the staff and asked them to leave the room. I then closed the door and proceeded to have a very long hot teary shower.

I was in hospital in the CCU ward for five days where I had tests most days, I saw all three of the teams that were now involved in my care every day. I was given a reprieve on the not lifting my son rule as it was deemed unreasonable to maintain. Providing that I got my mum over to help for a few weeks and followed the post heart attack cardiac rehab guide, increasing the weight gradually up to ten kilograms. My son was the only exception to that rule provided I limited the amount of times he was picked up. They told me to get rid of his cot, highchair and change table, providing steps for him to use to get on, off, in and out of things instead. So that is what we did; I went home, my mum flew out two days later and stayed for two weeks.

My one-year-old had to grow up very quickly. He was so good, just took it all in his stride; slept in a toddler bed – only fell out a few times; sat up at the table like a big boy and climbed into the big four-wheeled drive where he just then needed lifting into his seat. We were so proud of my six-year-old; he helped lift his brother in and out of the bath, and onto whatever else he needed help with. It has been hard on both kids and I had to explain that I could no longer lift, carry, piggy-back my oldest ever again, which in turn puts more strain on my husband as they go to him for all of the carrying type fun that we use to share.

The boss of my ward was very supportive and even though they couldn't renew my contract, they got me every piece of sick leave, carers leave and holiday days left to pay me until the end of my contract. I couldn't have asked for better treatment from those looking after me, to those who came to visit me from my ward; it made the hospital stay more bearable.

After a month of resting, doing my cardiac rehab duties and trying to behave myself with my new restrictions. I started an online vaccination course and started to apply for jobs. I got a job in a GP surgery a month or so later. It wasn't what I wanted to do, it wasn't the job that I dreamed of and it wasn't a job that was going to help me move forward in my career. I struggled with this for a long time and I would constantly get reminders of what I wasn't able to do anymore. This is where the Facebook Australian SCAD forum helped me so much. I could have a big whinge, cry, ask questions; just to connect with people who really did know what I was going through and the replies that I would get sometimes brought me to tears. I stopped feeling so alone and utterly helpless in my situation, just reading what other people wrote and their situations made me feel stronger and to know that this group of strangers were there to back me up was a tremendous relief.

One year on and apart from indigestion related chest pain, I am doing alright. I have had two visits back to ED, one early on and the other nearly six months later for chest pain. Both times, there was nothing new to be found. I am still waiting for the genetic testing to come back and have been monitored closely by all teams involved in my care. The other aneurysms are being monitored and haven't changed in size as yet so apart from the appointments, I have pretty much forgotten about them. No point in worrying if the medical teams aren't.

I have gone on to complete my certificate IV in training and assessing and looking at potential clinical nurse educator roles, which I would never have done if I was still working in the hospital and had my contract renewed or got to do my paramedics. Who knows, maybe I will enjoy doing that even more.

I honestly think that I am a stronger person now and that our marriage is even stronger than before, and that we are closer than ever. I feel bad that I can't help out with the heavy stuff that I use to anymore but know that he would rather have me around than not at all. I have also learnt not to be such a stubborn, independent person and that it's OK to ask for assistance and not feel embarrassed when I can't do something.

Sometimes, I wish that my boys didn't have to grow up so quickly but they have taken it in their stride and seem to be stronger and more independent (which is all we can ask in the end as parent I guess). It wasn't the end of the world; after all, I have moved forward and am just changing the path that we travel down instead. I appreciate life more and cherish moments more now than previously.

I would say for new survivors: don't try to go it alone, it's too big a thing to have the weight of it on your shoulders. Let people help, have a support network around you and get in touch with other survivors it really does help. Time does heal and even though my path has changed, I feel better about where it is now headed. The first anniversary was a big hurdle for me. I thought that I would just breeze through, but it did take me a week to get over what I had gone through in that previous year. I think some of it was also relief that I had made it through the year and that I was still here and doing ok. With each month that passes I feel stronger and more confident in myself again.

I am so grateful to my family and close friends, the prayers that were answered and the support group on Facebook. It would have been such a harder and slower journey without you, so thank you.

Julie Robertson – 2nd April 2015 – Aged 61

My name is Julie Robertson and I had a heart attack caused by SCAD – Spontaneous Coronary Artery Dissection – 2nd April 2015.

I was 61, I have been an RN for nearly 40 years and I had NEVER heard of SCAD. I had no risk factors. I weighed 50 kgs, I had no cholesterol problems and although I wouldn't call myself super fit, I was active. I have never smoked, never added salt to my cooking and tried to eat healthy – with some treats occasionally, but only small amounts. I walked every day, worked part-time and went to Curves about three times a week. I did have high blood pressure but it became so low, I was taken off medication.

2nd April began like any other day. I went for a walk and went to Curves and did some shopping. I was working the following day, Good Friday.

That night, when I ate dinner, I wasn't very hungry, so I only had a small meal. I was relaxed, watching TV – my husband was on the computer in the next room. I leant over with my right hand to pick up my phone on the coffee table and I had a sudden shooting pain down my left arm and I was nauseated at the same time! The pain and nausea wasn't severe but it was sudden and I felt both at the same time. I had no chest pain. I remember sitting there thinking, *I can't be having a heart attack – I have no risk factors.* I sat and thought, *I haven't strained my arm, as I was doing nothing, and I'm nauseated too for no apparent reason.* I had no shortness of breath...but the pain and nausea was still there. As my husband entered the room, I decide I was being silly – I could very well be having a heart attack, I knew women often don't get chest pain and have other symptoms – so I told him. I remember saying, "Something isn't right, I have pain down my left arm and I'm nauseated, I might be having a heart attack." On asking what I wanted to do, I just replied, "Go to hospital now."

My husband thought it would be quicker to drive me himself; we lived about 15 minutes from the Austin Hospital, where I worked. As we were driving there, the pain increased in my arm, it felt heavy and the nausea was worse. I was bent over, taking deep breaths and rubbing my arm – which was pointless but instinct, I guess…and even if I had thought of taking Aspirin, we had none in the house – as a nurse, I knew of all the side effects and only took Panadol for pain. Looking back, I think I was just so stunned, I wasn't thinking clearly, it all felt unreal.

I walked into the ER, holding my arm as if it were broken. My husband walked over to the triage nurse who was already occupied and interrupted her to tell her I might be having a heart attack. Quickly, someone came to the next window and as we were explaining my symptoms, I went pale and felt clammy.

I was wheeled into a cubicle. An ECG showed I had a 'cardiac event'. I had intravenous lines put in, I was given Aspirin, morphine and something for the nausea – and bloods were taken. Within a short time, I had an angiogram done – and that's when I was told I had a "tear in an artery wall", that it was too small to stent and that it would heal with medication. The pain went as soon as the dye for the angiogram was inserted – the flushing of the dye in the artery clears the blockage caused possibly by a clot.

I was admitted to the Coronary Care Ward. I remember going to move myself across to the bed but was quickly told not to, they would do everything – which I knew as a nurse but I think I was in shock and just not thinking clearly. My vitals, pulse, blood pressure and cardiac rhythms, were monitored – and because of the medication they gave to slow the heart, I didn't get much sleep as the monitor beeped every time I dozed off as my pulse would slow too much!!!

Once the pain was gone, I didn't feel as if I had a 'heart attack', it all felt unreal. I had frequent blood tests, as my cardiac enzymes kept rising, and I was told they would keep taking bloods until the cardiac enzymes started to drop in number – that the higher the number was, the more heart damage I had!!! Not very reassuring… I wondered were the staff more informative as I was a nurse too. Or did they do this with everyone. But then I was also told the damage may not be permanent, which was reassuring. I was told I had, "significant" heart damage.

Initially, I just popped every pill given to me, it was all a bit of a blur, I know I took quite a few magnesium tablets initially, but these weren't long term. But others were – Aspirin, Plavix, Ramipril, Metoprolol and Atorvastatin. I was told the two blood pressure medications slow the heart, so it isn't working too hard and the anti-cholesterol medication helps heal the torn artery – and Plavix and Aspirin to stop clots from forming. I was happy to take anything to help my heart heal.

I was admitted Easter Thursday evening and was discharged Easter Monday. I had no further pain in hospital, I wasn't on the monitor for long, but I did feel 'safe' in the hospital.

When I was home, my husband thought, *All fixed, everything is back to normal*. I wasn't told about any restrictions and I was told I could go back to work two weeks after my heart attack…but you don't bounce back that quick.

I found I tired more, I needed to rest more. The first night home, I had pain down my left arm when I was going to bed – I eventually worked out the cold triggered pain – in a hospital, the temperature control is set. I had pain in my legs – Atorvastatin can cause pain in your limbs – I was constipated soon after I had my heart attack – thanks to the side effects of Atorvastatin again – and although I could fall asleep watching TV, I would be wide awake in bed!!!

I went to Cardiac Rehab, which helped give me some confidence in how much exercise to do – the rehab isn't really catered for SCAD patients but I found it still helpful.

Listen to your body, it will tell you if you are doing too much and when you need to rest.

Work? I didn't go back in two weeks – how could I work as a nurse if I was still getting heart symptoms? I used up my sick leave and then, as work was my only stress, I retired early.

But my cardiologist was happy with me, I was booked in for a heart ultrasound, which showed no damage to the heart, and in July, I had another angiogram, which showed the dissection had healed. In August, my medication was reduced to Aspirin, Ramipril and Atorvastatin.

I did have some left arm pain, initially 4–5 times a week, but the pain didn't last long and it wasn't strong pain, more of an ache, a 'twinge'; when I had it, I would rest and take some deep breaths and it will go. I took nitro spray four times. The pain did lessen as time went on. After six months, it was only occasionally and two years out, it's now only rarely.

But we are all different. We are different ages, have different levels of fitness and have different backgrounds. But know you aren't alone. Some doctors and cardiologists can be unsympathetic and are only focused on what is the 'norm' for the usual heart attack patients. The one place I knew I would get understanding and unquestioning support is from the Australian SCAD Survivors Facebook site and many of us are happy to meet up or just talk to you.

How am I now two years post-SCAD? As I said, I rarely have any symptoms now, I walk every day, I don't like hills, but then I never did, and I'm back at Curves three times a week. I now have two beautiful grandsons who are five weeks apart in age, one lives in another state, which is probably just as well, as I look after 11-month-old Oliver four times a week while his mum goes to university and studies. I still sometimes have trouble falling asleep but not as much as before. My GP has taken me off the Atorvastatin, as my cholesterol has always been 'normal', I am trying to lower it even more to make my cardiologist happy. Life is good, you might see life differently and your life might not be quite the same – but it's still good!

Tabitha Schultz – 19th October 2015 – Aged 34

"34-year-old woman from Broken Hill, suspected NSTEMI, three months postpartum, no family history."

"Oh, you're so young!"

"Who has your baby now?"

These are the things that I heard over and over again on that day in October 2015 as I was transferred from Broken Hill Base Hospital, to the ambulance, to the RFDS flight, to the ambulance again, admission and finally the cardiac ward at Royal Adelaide Hospital. How did I end up here?

In July 2015, I'd given birth to my 4th baby, Ina Rosalie. It was a perfect birth with no assistance needed until the placenta was expelled and the bleeding wouldn't stop. I'd experienced a postpartum haemorrhage previously, so while it was a little worrying when I lost consciousness and needed an iron transfusion a few days later due to anaemia, everything was more or less ok. I was recovering well; my daughter was doing all the right things and by about three months, I had regained mobility and was starting to feel like my old self.

My husband, Andrew, and I decided to buy a rowing machine as a way of fitting in some good cardio and muscle strength building at home. Putting it together was a workout in itself, but I enjoyed seeing my form and power increase over those first few weeks. I had said to my husband, "I don't want to end up having a heart attack or getting diabetes in later life because we didn't bother to get on this now." Ha!

We'd had a bumpy 18 months prior to this. Andrew had appendicitis in March 2014 which lead to the discovery of a rare bowel cancer. A hemicolectomy was advised, and his recovery, with infections, was harrowing. We'd decided due to the physical difficulty of the pregnancy and birth of my 3rd child that we would pull up stumps there and have no more, but for whatever reason, in September that year, I found myself unexpectedly pregnant. After the initial shock, we found ourselves looking forward to the unplanned surprise, picking names and making plans, and then I started bleeding. "It's just a miscarriage," I was told in the emergency room, because hey, that's no biggie, happens all the time. While still deciding if we would actively seek to add a 4th child to the family, I was pregnant again. The bleeding started again, but this time it was an unviable twin being expelled, and we were having a baby girl. Andrew's routine colonoscopy a year post the initial surgery revealed a frightening number of polyps, and the surgeons wanted to act fast. The surgery was supposed to be a few weeks before my due date, but we bargained and it was set for six weeks after the baby's birth. We sent him off to Adelaide for the removal of his entire large bowel. He was thirty at the time, too young for this they said. He returned home two weeks later, and thankfully, the recovery was uncomplicated.

Because of the bumps in the road, when three months postpartum rolled around, I wanted to celebrate! I invited friends around for a cheesecake party. The premise was simple: bring a cheesecake, we all sample each other's cheesecakes and take home a variety of leftovers. SO. MUCH. CHEESECAKE. Bliss! Things were getting better.

The following day was Sunday. I was sitting at the back of the church service with my three-month-old; she was lying on the floor, smiling, kicking and making those beautiful baby sounds. I sat enjoying all of her beautiful 'babiness'. My left arm began to ache. That happened sometimes, and I thought I'd probably pinched a nerve or something when I'd been rowing. The pain intensified, right down to my fingers, a deep heavy aching pain that I couldn't alleviate. At the same time, my chest started to burn a little and my throat felt sore. I'm getting that cold the kids have I rationalised, as my whole body began to experience malaise. Everything felt heavy and I wanted to throw up. I told my husband that I was really not feeling good, and that I should probably go home. First though, I thought I'd go lie down in a separate room and just see if it would get better, it didn't. I googled heart attack symptoms while scolding myself for being such a hypochondriac. As if I would have a heart attack. I've just injured my arm, I'm getting a cold, and the feeling of doom is anxiety because I am making up far-fetched scenarios about heart attacks. I felt shaky and overly warm.

I sent Andrew a message telling how I was feeling. "In case I die, you can tell them what was going on," I said. I'm so funny, hilarious even. It wasn't getting better. My Google search scared me some because my symptoms were actually consistent with cardiac events. I knew it wasn't a heart attack though. Still the Heart Association's ad from years ago, 'I wish I could have my heart attack again' or something like that, was playing in my head. I asked Andrew to go get an emergency nurse friend of ours who was in the congregation. It wasn't long before she suggested that it wouldn't hurt to go to emergency. I didn't want to. I mean the baby would need feeding, the kids needed dinner, and it was just unnecessary fuss. My friend gently persisted, encouraging me that it wouldn't waste anyone's time, and even if it was just anxiety, that's ok. All the advertisements about anxiety attacks were also playing in my head, along with the government's recent attack on emergency departments, planning to charge fees for non-emergency consultations. I didn't want to be a bother!

However, I eventually agreed to go. I protested as I walked past triage – "I go straight in? What about other people who need to be here more?" Apparently, I was the top of the triage list this day.

"Describe your chest pain," they said.

"It feels like when you're really unfit and you go for a run," I told them.

An ECG was normal, "It's probably not your heart." I felt a mixture of shame and relief.

"Are you an athlete?" they asked.

"No," I laughed, "Why?"

"Oh, it's just that your heart rate is a little slow."

That's odd, I thought. It's normally around 65bpm at rest, though it had been faster the past few months as my blood restored itself. Blood pressure was OK, all vital signs good. The doctor suspected reflux, though I assured them that I was well-acquainted with reflux and this ain't it. Nonetheless, I was given antacids and some numbing stuff to drink. I started feeling better after lying there for a while. The team concluded that the diagnosis was confirmed, and that the rest was probably due to stress, being a new mum and having an unwell husband and so on. Unfortunately, because they'd taken bloods on arrival to check for cardiac enzymes, they had to keep me for six hours. So annoying! I was relieved though to tell Andrew when he came in that it's nothing. He left the baby with me because she needed a feed, and would arrange for a friend to pick us up later. When I went to the bathroom sometime later, the symptoms started again. My chest burned, my arm ached, but after more lying down, I felt OK. "Well at least it's a chance to have a nap," I told myself and closed my eyes.

Six hours were up. There'd been a shift change and the new doctor prepared my discharge summary for the GP. I was directed to take antacids to reduce symptoms, and due to the bradycardia and some detected arrhythmia, the discharge summary recommended later investigation with a Holter monitor, but importantly, acute coronary syndrome was definitely ruled out. We just had to wait for the blood results before I could go.

Suddenly, everything was turned upside down. The doctor came in, holding aloft a white docket with a look of shock on his face. "This paper here tells us that you've had a heart attack, and a proper one at that." I heard his words but surely it was a joke? The machine was broken? The test unreliable?

"Your machine must be broken," I told him. "Look, I feel fine now! Do it again." So, they took more blood, and tested again. My progress notes say: 'checked again due to very unexpected result'. This couldn't possibly be because of all the cheesecake the night before, could it? Had my love of donuts done this? Maybe I'd exercised too much the last week and made it happen. I joked about Andrew's health history and this heart attack they were saying that I had. We're having the things we are supposed to experience in 40 years' time! Maybe we're getting it out of the way and will have no more troubles from here. That'd be nice. I had to call Andrew and tell him. There was no way for him not to be freaked out, obviously. I reassured him that I was fine and I'd probably be home tomorrow anyway. Then they made me cry.

"You can't breastfeed anymore with this medication that we need to give you. You must have the medication because right now your heart tissue is dying, and we need to stop that from happening." The words I never expected to hear. We'd worked so hard for an intervention-free birth, delayed cord clamping: the works. She was a vaginal birth after caesarean (VBAC) baby and to birth freely in that case takes bucket loads of stubbornness and fortitude! Despite my blood loss, she was breastfeeding beautifully, and now that was to be taken away in an instant! I was stable enough that they let me express as much milk as I could for the next feed; a midwife came and sat with me while I did. We talked about Ina May Gaskin, a famous midwife, with whom my daughter shares a name. It was a good moment in what had suddenly become quicksand.

I was transferred to ICU, around midnight I think. I had my baby and I was not letting go. I became aware of raised voices arguing near me. "We can't have a baby in ICU. It's hospital policy." At the time, I wasn't sure who was on my side, but my baby wasn't going anywhere if I could help it.

"She's quiet, she'll be no trouble to other patients," I told them. "But I don't have anything to feed her now." Suddenly I was unable to care for her basic needs (save cuddles) and reluctant to ask for help because I knew someone didn't want her there.

The next morning saw doctors, nurses, Andrew and the kids come up. I told the kids, aged six, five and two, "My heart's a bit loose," a line from Peppa Pig. It was simple and they were concerned but OK. Luckily, I have a number of friends who were nurses or other health professionals at the hospital, and I had plenty of visitors to distract me and help with the baby.

Instead of being sent home (I had such hopes!), I found out that I was to be flown to Adelaide for further investigation. I've never been on a plane before. In the past, I had joked that it would suck to have my first flight as a patient. Ha ha ha ha ha… ha. Now it was happening. A midwife, who knows me well, and the lactation consultant came to discuss what I'd do with the baby and breastfeeding. Apparently, I could take her to Adelaide. "Good," I said, "that's what I want to do." However, the reality of tests, being unable to feed her myself or even prepare her food, no family to assist, a big old hospital full of germs… I made the heart-breaking decision to leave her here. Three friends would share her care while Andrew looked after the three older kids. I still can't talk about this part without tears and a tightening of my chest. Leaving her was the hardest thing I've ever done. The one piece of good news in that was that the lactation consultant had spoken to a pharmacist at the Women and Children's Hospital in Adelaide and was confident that they would find drugs which would make breastfeeding viable, if I wished.

One of the ambos who came for my transfer was my neighbour. It's good living in a small town! She even helped me get a selfie with the plane. My first flight you know! That flight, far out; that was not how I thought my first experience of air travel would pan out! I was strapped to a stretcher so I had to strain my head to look out the window. I was NOT missing this experience no matter what had just happened. So, with tears streaming, my heart breaking in a different way because it felt so wrong to be flying away from my flesh and blood, and a sense of wonder at the physical forces that held this noisy tin can in the air, and sheer excitement at the experience of flight, I made it to Adelaide.

When I arrived, it seemed no one had told them the baby was staying home. I was asked several times: "Do you have kids?" "Where is the baby?" "Oh, why didn't you bring her? We were looking forward to a baby on the ward." Each question opened the wound again.

In Adelaide, I found out just how slowly hospitals move, like a creaking old ship with an anonymous captain and a really bad cook. An angiogram confirmed the cardiologist's suspicion that a cardiac artery had torn. I used the information they'd given me and google said it was a SCAD. The doctor's rounds the next day confirmed this. A group of online friends who happened to live in Adelaide organised themselves so that I had visitors each day. Someone to talk to, food that was palatable. Fruit! Why don't hospitals provide decent fruit!!! Such a relief to receive fruit, in more ways than one. Other friends from Adelaide made their way over. I had a steady stream to keep my spirits high. Friends from all over sent me cards (and hand spun yarn!) too, I never had to be truly alone.

My blood pressure ended up too low for blood pressure meds, and my intent to recommence breastfeeding along with no serious reoccurrence of symptoms meant that after IV Heparin for five days, I was able to dodge long term blood thinners save the ubiquitous aspirin. A junior doctor told me "Unfortunately, we can't test these things on breastfeeding mothers, ethically you know, so we have to guess." Unfortunately?! That made me laugh, but I appreciated the medical point of view as well. Damn ethics. The junior doctors were a helpful bunch to talk to. They were probably my age and younger, so while all the staff were telling me, "Oh you're so young!" I was thinking, 'Wait, are you old enough to be out of high school?' The dashing Justin Trudeau was elected Prime Minister of Canada that week, and I thought, *Maybe there's hope for the world yet.*

I was reluctant in many ways to tell my friends what had happened. Who would believe it? And if they did, would they think that I was dying? How do you break such news? My smartphone surely saved my sanity. I instagrammed a picture so that they could see I was actually still alive, while sharing the news. The women caring for my baby send me photos and updates; I could Skype my kids. I found a SCAD survivors' support group online and became acquainted with other people's stories. I listened to audiobooks saved on my phone. Granted they were kids' books, but who doesn't love a bit of David Tennant narrating anything?

By Friday, I wanted to be home. There was one more test they said, and I needed to stay because I couldn't have it in Broken Hill. I pleaded to go, promising to come back at a later time for the rest, if I could just go now. Finally, the head doctor agreed – provided I pass a modified stress test. I was up for it! The picture in front of the treadmill was painted by Jack Absalom, an artist who lives just houses away from me. A desert scene. I decided that this was me walking home! I walked and walked and passed the test! Home for me! I needed to be home as Andrew was flying into Adelaide that next week for follow-up from his recent surgery anyway. However, by the time the tests were done and I was clear to go, it was late in the arvo. I'd be there another day, at least, and weekend flights to Broken Hill were scarce.

The shift change brought me an angel. A nurse with red curly hair, a freckled face and a pregnant belly. Surely the most beautiful woman I'd ever seen. She spent the next hours busily arranging my discharge, as if the most important thing in the world was to get me home to my baby! The pharmacist came with my meds, there were still some seats on the 6pm flight. Andrew booked one, they got me a taxi and I was out of there!! A few selfies at the exit, a taxi ride to the airport and I was going home!!

The next weeks are a fog now. Beta-blockers and the process of recovery made me drowsy, and my mind was still trying to process all that had happened. I remember that the online SCAD group was crucial at the time. A message at 3am when I couldn't sleep because of with what-ifs, would always be answered by people who'd been there and come through. I saw women who were back to their lives, running marathons even! Such encouragement for me. I spent my time looking after my kids, trying to re-establish breastfeeding with the baby (it took a month but we got there and at almost 2, she's still going!), and I dyed wool to crochet some anatomically correct hearts. My kitchen was covered in blood-coloured dye while I did this. It was macabre and also, hilarious. I took that to be a part of my healing process, a way to let myself work through some of those thoughts and feelings. I felt like a dork giving one of them to my cardiologist but hey, it's about the process and I'm glad that I did it.

Friends arranged to cover things like the cost of the flight home, amazing because Andrew's recent surgery and the birth had depleted our savings, and also gifted us money to engage a house cleaner for a while. People provided meals, especially while I was away, and tried to help where they could. A friend walked with me weekly while I healed and regained fitness. I'm so grateful for all the practical support that we received. I've probably forgotten significant things, but it all helped in our family's recovery from the event.

A few months later, I had the opportunity to attend cardiac rehab. If there is anything any heart attack survivor should do, it is to participate in cardiac rehab. Sure, it was me and a bunch of elderly men and women but we made it work. Of course, there were participants (and even educators) who thought I was a physio, instead of a participant, but in time everyone got used to having a young'un in their midst. CR helped me regain confidence in my body again, and to discover that while I don't love exercise, the chance to focus on strengthening my body was a gift! I felt safe with a crash cart in the same room and the emergency room 100 meters away. There was nothing to lose and everything to gain.

I've just passed 18 months. My heart is healthy and strong. I attend the local gym three times a week for a few reasons. One, it's a good chance to listen to podcasts without having to think about where little people are (my gym has a crèche, it's wonderful!), it's an opportunity to school my body and let it know that it will not hold me back from the rest of life, and lastly, I know that if SCAD or something else should try to thwart me again, I'm going to be in the best position to be a survivor again.

I'm looking at going back to University soon when my 3rd child starts preschool. I'm hoping to study in the areas of health promotion and rehab, because now these things mean something to me. SCAD might have been a potential stop sign for me if things had turned out differently but they didn't, thank goodness! Hopefully, my experience can help others to be survivors in the future too.

Pamela McKenzie – 20th April 2014 – Aged 43

At the time of my SCAD, I was only 43 years of age, fit, healthy and with no personal or genetic risk factors for a heart attack and this is my story about how I had a Spontaneous Coronary Artery Dissection (SCAD) in my left main artery which caused me to have a heart attack.

For Easter, I had all four of my children (Aaron – 24, Kalila – 22, Jacinta – 18 and Becky – 16) plus my grandkids (Kael – four and Melody – three) staying with me for the Easter weekend. Unfortunately, my husband is a FIFO worker and was away working in the Pilbara at the time. It was great having everyone around for the weekend and I'd been looking forward to this weekend for ages; we don't get to all be in the one place at the same time much anymore.

On Easter Sunday (20th of April), I woke up early and enjoyed waiting for all the kids and grandkids to wake up and part take in our traditional Easter Egg hunt. After the grandkids had located all the Easter eggs, we all sat down at the outdoor table and myself, the kids and grandkids all laughed and had a great time colouring in the Easter colouring-in books and head bands whilst enjoying the recently-found Easter eggs. I thought I would wait until a bit later in the day before I ate mine as I'm not such a fan of eating chocolate first thing in the morning.

It was awesome watching everyone having so much fun. As it was a Sunday morning, we headed down to the Busselton jetty markets to look around. It was nice and busy down there and I bumped into an old friend who was at the markets with her daughter. We had a quick chat and caught up before we parted ways to follow our kids. Melody (my granddaughter) was on the bouncy castle when my sister

(Naomi) texted me to say she was already at my place waiting for us with our mum, as we were planning on having a big family lunch at my place to celebrate Easter lunch. I replied to her text to let her know that we were on our way home and would meet her there.

I'd had a nasty headache for most of the morning, but dismissed it as I had nasty headaches for the last few weeks and I just put it down to perimenopause.

We left the markets and when we arrived at home, my mum and sister had left to go visit an aunt of mine who lived close by while they were waiting for us. I sent them a text to let them know that we had now arrived and they could come back.

We went into the house and everyone was really excited about Easter lunch. My brother (Graham) sent me a text asking what he and Jodi (his beautiful new bride) should bring for lunch. I replied and then put some chicken drumsticks in the oven to cook. Once lunch was cooking, I gathered up a load of washing and took it outside to the laundry and started a load of washing in the machine. The washing machine was located outside in a laundry room which was attached to a granny flat. As I went to put the load of washing in the machine, I felt a twinge in my chest (almost like a click) thought it was a bit weird, but just ignored it.

I walked back into the house and felt a sudden intense extreme pain just to the left of the centre of my chest in a specific area. This pain radiated down both arms and then I felt a wave of nausea wash over me. I sat down on the couch, put my head in my hands and tried deep breathing to see if it would ease the symptoms. When this didn't work and I started to feel worse, I got up and told Becky (my youngest daughter) I didn't feel well and was going to lie down. Becky helped me to take off my boots and then I laid down on the bed with my feet raised up on the top of the bed head.

I started to become concerned when the symptoms did not ease and I started to feel myself breaking into a cold sweat. When Kalila came to check in on me, I asked if she could please get me my mobile phone. She went and found it, and brought it to me. When she left the room, I then rang for an ambulance. When she came back to see how I was doing, I then informed her that I had rung for an ambulance as I thought I may need to be taken to hospital.

I then asked Kalila to please text Naomi and let her know not to come around as lunch would be cancelled. Naomi and my mum arrived shortly afterwards.

The ambulance and paramedics arrived within five minutes, gave me an aspirin and a spray of GTN (a spray used for angina attacks) under my tongue (I found out later that this was an unusual procedure since I had no risk factors and was so young, but this was probably what saved my life). The paramedics attached an ECG machine to me and said that I had an inverted T-wave on the read out. They took my temperature as I was being wheeled on the stretcher into the ambulance and it was slightly below normal at 35.5 degrees. Kalila travelled to the hospital with me in the ambulance. I arrived at the hospital around 12:30pm. The nurses were sure there was nothing wrong with me as I had presented at the hospital with absolutely no symptoms remaining. They inserted a cannula into my arm and took some blood to check my troponin levels (this gives a reading for heart damage).

When the results finally came in, they shocked the nurses in the emergency department as the initial reading showed that I had an equivocal result. I was also a bit shocked as I had no symptoms since I had been in the emergency department and had pretty much convinced myself that I was fine.

When the attending doctor saw the results, she told me I would likely be sent to Bunbury hospital as it was a long weekend and the Busselton hospital didn't have access to a cardiologist and I was so young. At this point, I asked Kalila to ring my husband (Shane) as I didn't want to worry him earlier while he was so far away in case there had been no problems.

My kids took turns to come and keep me company in the emergency department. I felt really guilty as this wasn't the day that I had planned for them.

As I had been joking around with my daughter since being admitted and had been in a light happy mood, one nurse told me I should be taking this much more seriously and 'didn't I realise how serious this was'.

The Busselton hospital then rang the Bunbury hospital to see if they would take me. Bunbury hospital's reply was that they would only take me if my enzyme levels didn't rise any further with the next set of results. I was then informed there could actually be a possibility that I could be sent to a Perth hospital.

The next troponin level test showed a rise again which meant that I needed to be flown to a Perth hospital via RFDS. Which at the time I found slightly amusing as I had just bought a raffle ticket at the markets that morning for the RFDS. I had been in the Busselton hospital emergency department for 12 hours by the time I was finally flown up to Perth.

I arrived at Royal Perth Hospital around 1am in the morning (such a long day). I had further blood tests taken and attached to another set of leads attached to me (this was the fourth set of leads and stickers I had attached to me during my adventure, but no one had removed any) I joked with the nurses that they would need to remove some before attaching anymore as there wasn't much skin left that wasn't covered in stickers. The best part was that their heart monitor machine was wireless so I could get up and move around without having to ask someone to detach and then reattach all the wires just so I could go to the toilet or shower.

After a few hours' sleep, I was told that I would now be needing to be on medications for the rest of my life and I would be undergoing further tests to find out exactly what had happened to cause my heart attack. The nurses mentioned that I would be undergoing an angiogram and described what that meant, at which point I was not so sure I wanted any of this anymore. Thankfully, they also told me that as it was a long weekend, I would probably need to wait until the following day before they could do the angiogram.

Thankfully, Shane was able to get on a flight and arrive at the hospital around 11am that morning as I was starting become pretty scared. I felt really guilty when I saw him as he had been on night shift and looked totally shattered. When I spoke with Shane earlier, I had told him I was OK and he mentioned that I was being too brave as I wasn't as OK as I was telling him, otherwise I wouldn't be getting flown to a Perth hospital. I was so relieved when he arrived as my bravado was starting to wear pretty thin at that point.

Fortunately, my kids had travelled back to Perth that day so they were also able to visit me and keep me company. My aunt, her husband and my cousin also dropped by to say hello. It was really good having so many visitors as it helped to distract me from thinking about the angiogram.

Shane stayed with me as long as he could, but he needed to head home (2.5 hours' drive) back to Busselton so he could shower and gather some clean clothes. I felt really guilty as he looked really stressed and totally exhausted.

The next morning (Tuesday), I was told that I was 8th on the list for the angiogram, but they would double check to see as the list numbering can change after a long weekend. I was really starting to panic as I was terrified about the angiogram. I had barely slept the night before as I was really anxious. I had some doctors come and ask me about what I had experienced during my heart attack as they struggled to figure out why someone who was fit and healthy, with no risk factors, could have a heart attack. I was sent off for an echo cardiogram prior to my surgery to see if there was any muscular damage to my heart.

When I got back from my echo cardiogram (an ultrasound of the heart muscles), I was really starting to wish I could just get up and leave, and wondered if I could just say that I didn't want to do it. Thankfully, Shane arrived just before I was taken for the angiogram as he helped to calm me down a bit. I was told that the procedure would only take about 30 minutes if the surgeon found nothing and only had to go in, look around and come back out again. I was pretty sure that this would be the case and this was how I tried to keep myself calm.

I was kept waiting in the waiting area outside the operating theatre for about an hour before I was finally wheeled into the room. The procedure was performed whilst I was awake and I was able to watch it on the TV screens right next to the trolley I was on. They put a general anaesthetic in my groin area where they wanted to go in and once that had started working, they entered the main artery there and put a camera all the way up to my heart. I was laying there for a while, watching the screens, trying to figure out what I was looking at and then asked the surgeon if it was worse than he first thought as I heard him saying that there was quite a bit of narrowing of the arteries, and he had asked for three stents of different sizes. He told me he would explain it all to me afterwards.

I was in the surgical theatre for an hour and a half whilst they inserted the stents into my left main coronary artery. After the surgery, I was taken back to another room close to the nurse's station to recover.

As I was being taken to my new room, we were wheeled past where my kids, sister and husband were waiting for me, the orderly pushing my bed stated happily, "Well, that must be your daughter." I have been told many times in the past how much my kids look like me. It was comforting to know they were all there waiting for me. Unfortunately, because I had been in surgery for so long, my kids had to leave soon afterwards. Thankfully, my husband was still there as he has this way of being able to calm me down when I get anxious.

Shane stayed for as long as he could, but had to leave to go back home again. Before Shane left, the surgeon came to see me to discuss what he had found in the surgery. He seemed nervous as he told me that I had had a spontaneous dissection in my left main coronary artery. He explained that this was really rare and he had never seen it before in his career, and kept reiterating how lucky I was to have survived. The surgeon also said that usually when damage is found that close to the heart, they usually perform a bypass, but they had

171

to put three stents in instead. I have been told since that there was no option but to use stents, as there really was no way to bypass all of the tear due to the positioning of it all.

I was not allowed to bend my right leg, where they went into the artery for the surgery, for nine hours afterwards so as not to snap the plastic tube that was in my artery. After six hours, they removed the tube; this involved placing a clamp over my groin on top of the artery to stop it from bleeding out and the clamp stayed on for 30 minutes. It made me really dizzy at one point, so they tipped the bed backwards to counter act the dizziness. After it was out, I was way too scared to move my leg to be able to sleep, not that sleep would have been easy anyway after such a shocking day. There was way too much to be able to take in to settle down and sleep properly.

The cardiologist came to see me the next morning and reiterated what the surgeon had said the day before, that what had happened to me was very rare, but where it had happened was even rarer. He mentioned that the echo cardiogram had shown that there was no damage to my heart and it still functions perfectly. I was told that I would be able to go home the following day (Thursday). I was really excited and a little bit nervous about going home. I was just looking forward to not being in the hospital hooked up to machines anymore.

On Thursday, I was released from hospital when Shane arrived to pick me up with all of my new medications. These were inclusive of aspirin, atorvastatin (for cholesterol – standard precaution for anyone after a heart attack), Ticagrelor (to stop my stents from blocking), metoprolol (to lower my heart rate and keep it steady as I had had some irregular rhythms in hospital), potassium (my blood test had shown my levels were a little low) and a GTN spray (for angina symptoms). I was told that under no circumstances was I to miss a dose of Ticagrelor as this could cause my stents to block and I would not get a second chance to take a missing dose. This was very confronting to hear.

On the way home, we stopped to chat with some old friends where I used to work on the way home. I was just so glad to finally be out of hospital.

Walking into the house when we got home was a little more confronting than I expected. Seeing our bed, where I laid after the heart attack, my boots on the floor where Becky and I had kicked them off, my watch on the side table as I had to take it off for the paramedics and the memories of laying there now knowing how close I had come to dying there. All I could think of was how horrible it would have been for Shane if that had been where I died... It was also extremely hard for me when I walked into the kitchen and saw that the kids had left their Easter eggs behind. I felt so guilty about ruining their Easter. They were so young, they shouldn't have the memory of almost losing their mum on Easter, and I certainly don't want them thinking of that every Easter. Easter is supposed to be fun for kids, it shouldn't be a horrible memory.

As hard as all of this has been on me, I know that it has been so much harder on those close to me. I feel like such a horrible person for putting them all through this, and the hardest thing to deal with has been that no one can tell me why. It is exceptionally hard to know that we have all gone through such an emotionally traumatic time, and there doesn't seem to be a reason for it. The closest that doctors can come to telling me why it might have happened has been to blame it on hormones.

This is why I have chosen to use this experience to try and help others by raising awareness of SCAD and hopefully be a link in the chain towards research being undertaken so that no one else has to go through the same thing as I have.

It was really hard for me to go from being such a stubbornly independent person to having to rely so heavily on everyone else around me. I always need to be aware of what length of time I will be away from home because I have to make sure I have enough medication on me, and I always have to take my GTN spray with me in case I get chest pain. Whilst at first, I was only able to exercise up to 70% of my capacity and only for 15 minutes so as not to strain anything. It was hard to deal with since I used to love going for bike rides with my husband and playing on my Wii with the Wii fit and Zumba games. I was very conscious of any pains in my chest and found that my fear limited me a lot to begin with. The knowledge that my body just randomly tried to kill me for no apparent reason means that I no longer trust my body to tell me if something is wrong. I never used to be the kind of person to cry before, but I have totally soaked my husband's shoulder in tears so many times now trying to understand what has happened to me. I have been exceptionally lucky in the fact that I have an amazing support network with my husband, kids, family and friends. I need all of this to be for a reason, so I'm choosing to make that reason one that will help others.

I have started an Australian SCAD survivors Facebook page for other survivors so that they don't have to feel isolated by this uncommon coronary event (SCAD) and they can talk to others who have been through the same things. This is a closed group. I have also created an open group for non-SCAD survivors to help them to learn more about and try to understand SCAD as well as a website for the general public (www.whatisscad.com.au) in the hopes of reaching other survivors who may not realise that they are not alone.

Thankfully, since I first wrote my story, they have now changed my medications and I don't bruise as easily, and the fatigue issues I was struggling with aren't as severe anymore. My life is almost back to normal except for the fear of the stents in my left main artery blocking, or having another SCAD. I do suffer slightly from anxiety since my SCAD and some events trigger a type of 'flashback' memory which is very hard to deal with. Mostly, I am a happy person and very determined, but it is hard to not worry. I am learning to deal with this better as every year passes.

ABBREVIATIONS / MEDICAL TERMS

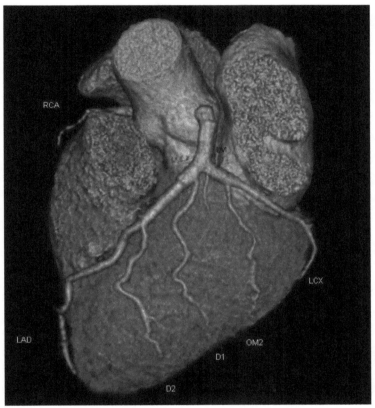

Picture Courtesy of Imaging Central – Morley W.A.

Coronary Arteries

LM	Left Main
LCX	Left Circumflex Artery
LAD	Left Anterior Artery
OM2	Obtuse Marginal branch
RCA	Right Coronary Artery
D1	Diagonal 1
D2	Diagonal 2

Angiogram	A coronary angiogram is a special x-ray of your heart the purpose of this is to look for abnormalities of heart muscle or heart valves and to see the coronary arteries are narrowed or blocked
CCU	Coronary Care Unit
Electrocardiogram	An electrocardiogram is a medical test that detects cardiac) abnormalities by measuring the electrical activity generated by the heart as it contracts. The machine that records the patient's ECG is called an electrocardiograph.
ED	Emergency Department at a hospital
GTN Spray	Glyceryl trinitrate (GTN) is a spray used to relieve angina (chest pain). When sprayed under the tongue, it relaxes and widens blood vessels in the heart and in the rest of the body.
ICU	Intensive Care Unit

MRI	A magnetic resonance imaging (MRI) scan is a common procedure used by hospitals around the world. MRI uses a strong magnetic field and radio waves to create detailed images of the organs and tissues within the body SCAD – Spontaneous Coronary Artery Dissection.
Sestamibi	Sestamibi Scan is used to examine the blood flow to the heart muscle before and after a stress test.
Statins	Statins are a class of medicines that are frequently used to lower blood cholesterol levels. They do this by blocking the action of a specific chemical in the liver that is necessary for making cholesterol.
Stents	A stent is a small mesh tube that's used to treat narrow or weak arteries. Arteries are blood vessels that carry blood away from your heart to other parts of your body. A stent is placed in an artery as part of a procedure called percutaneous coronary intervention (PCI), also known as coronary angioplasty.

Takotsubo Cardiomyopathy	Otherwise known as stress-induced cardiomyopathy or broken-heart syndrome, it occurs when the main pumping chamber of the heart fails and balloons with blood. There is a strong relationship between the syndrome and physical or emotional stress, such as death of a loved one, a serious accident, a sudden illness or a natural disaster, hence the name.
Troponin Levels	A troponin test measures the levels troponin T or troponin I proteins in the blood. These proteins are released when the heart muscle has been damaged, such as occurs with a heart attack. The more damage there is to the heart, the greater the amount of troponin T and I there will be in the blood.
Optical Coherence Tomography (OCT)	A technique that captures three-dimensional images at very fine (micrometres) resolution. The use of relatively long-wavelength light allows it to penetrate deeply, making it very suitable for visualising the detailed structure of blood vessels and hence to locate dissections (tears in the blood vessel) as occurs in SCAD

sufferers. OCT is often the preferred technique for diagnosing SCAD, although Intravascular Ultrasound (IVUS) may be a safer alternative diagnostic tool.

Useful Website Links

Worldwide group (for survivors only) –
https://www.facebook.com/groups/SCADsupport/
SCAD Alliance (open group) –
https://www.facebook.com/SCADalliance/
Mayo Group (open group) –
https://www.facebook.com/SCADMayoClinic/?fref=ts
SCAD Website *https://www.whatisscad.com.au*

Notes

This is where you can write down information given to you by the medical staff in the hospital so that you have a record you can refer back to when needed.

Printed in the USA
CPSIA information can be obtained
at www.ICGtesting.com
LVHW070155170923
758231LV00036BB/525